SONGS OF FELLOWSHIP

BOOK FIVE

KINGSWAY MUSIC
EASTBOURNE

The words of most of the songs in this publication
are covered by the Church Copyright Licence

United Kingdom
CCL UK Ltd, P.O. Box 1339, Eastbourne, East Sussex, BN21 4YF

United States
CCL Inc., 6130 NE 78th Court, Suite C11, Portland, Oregon 97218

Australasia
CCL Asia Pacific Ltd, P.O. Box 1254, Castle Hill, NSW 2154

ISBN 0 85476 549 2
(Music edition ISBN 0 85476 550 6)

Scripture quotations adjacent to some of the songs
in this volume are from the Holy Bible, New International Version,
copyright © International Bible Society 1973, 1978, 1984.
Published by Hodder & Stoughton and
used by permission.

Produced by Bookprint Creative Services
P.O. Box 827, BN21 3YJ, England for
KINGSWAY MUSIC LTD
Lottbridge Drove, Eastbourne, E. Sussex BN23 6NT
Printed in Great Britain

Important notes

Order of songs

The songs appear in alphabetical order by first line (letter by letter), not necessarily by author's title, for easy use in praise and worship meetings. An index of titles and first lines is included at the back, along with other useful indexes and chord charts.

To further facilitate the use of this book, all two-page songs and hymns appear on facing pages to avoid turning over, while maintaining the alphabetical order.

Scripture references

References – listed in biblical order – are to the key Bible passages quoted or echoed in the songs, and to some passing references. In many cases the whole Bible passage will repay further exploration, beyond the verses listed. A full index to the Scripture references is provided at the back of the book.

1.

All consuming fire

Ex 3:14; Deut 4:24; Heb 12:29

Capo 1 (Bm)

Randy Wright

With awe

All con-sum-ing fi - re, You're my heart's de-
You're my me-di - ta - tion, and my con-sol-

si - re, } and I love You dear - ly, dear - ly
a - tion,

Lord. Lord.

Glo - ry to the— Lamb,— I ex-

2.
All I once held dear
(Knowing You)

Phil 3:7-11

Graham Kendrick

Smoothly ♩ = 65

Verse

1. All I once held dear, built my life up - on, all this world re-veres, and wars to own, all I once thought gain I have coun-ted— loss; spent and worth-less now, com - pared to this.

Chorus

Know-ing You, Jesus, know - ing You, there is no great-er thing. You're my

all, You're the best,— You're my joy, my right-eous-ness, and I love You, Lord.—

— 2. Now my love You, Lord,— love, You, Lord.

2. Now my heart's desire
   Is to know You more,
   To be found in You
   And known as Yours.
   To possess by faith
   What I could not earn,
   All-surpassing gift
   Of righteousness.

3. Oh, to know the power
   Of Your risen life,
   And to know You in
   Your sufferings.
   To become like You
   In Your death, my Lord,
   So with You to live
   And never die.

3.

All that I am

Rom 12:1; 2 Cor 12:10; Gal 2:20; Phil 4:19

Capo 3 (D)

With feeling

James Wright

All that I am I lay be - fore You; all I pos - sess, Lord I con - fess is no-thing with - out You. Sa-viour and King, I now en - throne You; take my life, my liv-ing sa-cri-fice to You. 1. Lord, be the

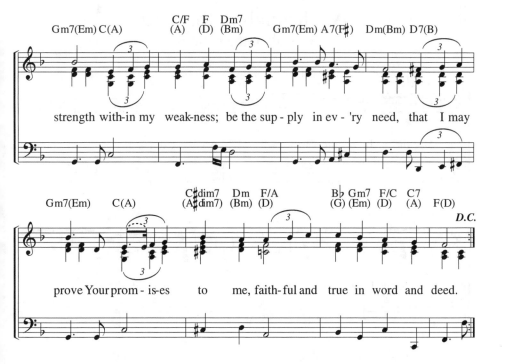

2. Into Your hands I place the future;
   The past is nailed to Calvary,
   That I may live in resurrection power,
   No longer I but Christ in me.

4.

All the ends of the earth
(Awaken the nations)

Ps 22: 27-28

David Fellingham

2. Who will not fear the Lord of glory,
   Or bring honour to His holy name?
   For God has spoken with integrity and truth,
   A word which cannot be revoked.

5. And He shall reign

Is 9:7; Dan 7:13;
Mt 24:30; 26:64;
Mk 13:26; 14:62;
Rev 1:13; 11:15; 22:5
Graham Kendrick

And He shall reign for ev - er, His throne and crown shall ev - er en - dure. And He shall reign for ev - er, and we shall reign with Him.

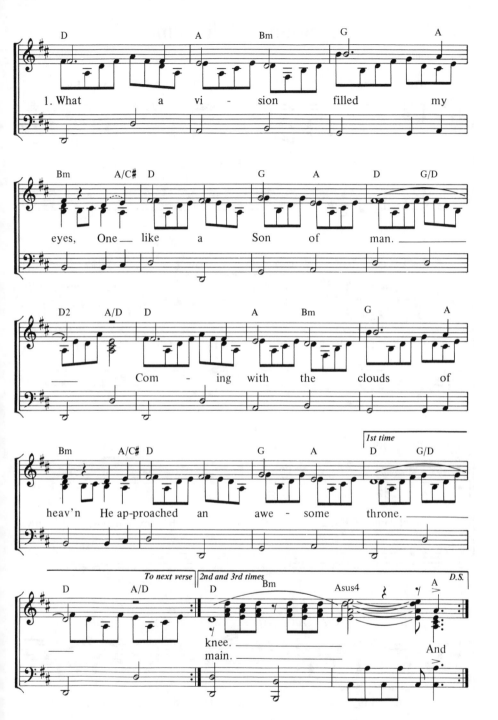

2. He was given sovereign power,
Glory and authority.
Every nation, tribe and tongue
Worshipped Him on bended knee.

3. On the throne for ever,
See the Lamb who once was slain.
Wounds of sacrificial love
Forever shall remain.

6.
Anointing, fall on me

Acts 10:44; 11:15

Donn Thomas

pow-er of_ the Ho - ly Ghost__ fall on me,__ a - noint-ing fall_ on

D.C. al Fine

me.　　　　A -

7. As we behold You

2 Cor 3:18

David Baroni

O Lord, our Lord,
    how majestic is your name in all
        the earth!
    You have set your glory
        above the heavens.

PSALM 8:1

8.

At the foot of the cross

Rom 5:8; 1 Cor 15:3
Heb 9:15; 1 Pet 3:18

Derek Bond

With a gentle rhythm

At the foot of the cross,___ I can hard-ly take___ it in,___ that the King of all___ cre-a-tion was dy-ing for___ my sin.___ And the pain and a-gon-y,___ and the thorns that pierced___ Your head,___ and the hard-ness of___ my sin-ful heart___ that left You there___ for dead.___

9.
Be free

2 Cor 3:17; Phil 1:6; 2:3

Joyfully

Dave Bilbrough

Be free in the love of God, let His Spi - rit flow with - in you. Be free in the love of God, let it fill your soul. Be free in the love of God, cel - e - brate His name with dan - cing. Be free in the love of God, He has made us whole.

2. God is gracious, He will lead us
   Through His power at work within us.
   Spirit, guide us, and unite us
   In the Father's love.

10.

Behold the Lord

Rev 1:14-15, 17-18; 4:8

Noel Richards & Gerald Coates

1. Be-hold the Lord u - pon His throne; His face is shi - ning like the sun. With
eyes bla-zing fire, and feet glow-ing bronze, His voice like might-y wa-ter roars.
Ho - ly, ho - ly, Lord God Al - migh-ty.
Ho - ly, ho - ly, we stand in awe of You.

2. The first, the last, the living One,
Laid down His life for all the world.
Behold He now lives for evermore,
And holds the keys of death and hell.
Holy, holy, Lord God Almighty.
Holy, holy, we bow before Your throne.

3. So let our praises ever ring
To Jesus Christ, our glorious King.
All heaven and earth resound as we cry:
"Worthy is the Son of God!"
Holy, holy, Lord God Almighty.
Holy, holy, we fall down at Your feet.

11. Be known to us in breaking bread

Mt 26:26; Mk 14:22; Lk 24:30;
Jn 6:54; 1 Cor 11:23; Rev 3:20

MANOAH

From Rossini (1792-1868)
(Greatorex Collection 1851)

1. Be — known to us in break-ing bread, but — do not then de - part; — Sa - viour, a - bide with us, and spread — Thy ta - ble in — our heart. —

2. There sup with us in love divine;
Thy body and Thy blood,
That living bread, that heavenly wine,
Be our immortal food.

James Montgomery (1771-1854)

12. Blessèd be the name of the Lord

Neh 9:5; Job 1:21; Prov 18:10

(The name of the Lord)

Capo 3 (D)

Lively

Clinton Utterbach

2. Glory to the name of the Lord,
   Glory to the name of the Lord.
   Glory to the name of the Lord,
   Most High.
   (Repeat)

3. Holy is the name of the Lord,
   Holy is the name of the Lord,
   Holy is the name of the Lord,
   Most High.
   (Repeat)

13. Blessed Jesus

Jn 4:14; Rev 5:12

Joey Holder

With a steady rhythm

1. Bles-sed Je-sus come to me, soothe my soul with songs of— peace.
As I look to You a-lone fill me with Your love.

Chorus

Glo-ri-ous, mar-vell-ous grace that res-cued— me;
ho-ly, wor-thy is the Lamb who died for me.

2. Mountains high and valleys low,
You will never let me go;
By Your fountain let me drink,
Fill my thirsty soul.

14. Bless the Lord, my soul

Ps 103: 1;3-4;8;10;13-14

Taizé

Bless the Lord, my soul, and bless His ho-ly name. Bless the Lord, my

soul, He res-cues me from death.

1. It is He who for-gives all your guilt, who heals ev-'ry one of your ills, who re-deems your life from the grave, who crowns you with love and com-pas-sion.

2. The Lord is com-pas-sion and love, slow to an-ger and rich in mer-cy. He does not treat us ac-cord-ing to our sins, nor re-pay us ac-cord-ing to our faults.

3. As a fa-ther has com-pas-sion on his child-ren, the Lord has pi-ty on those who fear Him;— for He knows of what we are made, He re-mem-bers that we are dust.

15.
Breathe on me

Jn 20:21-22

Tina Pownall

2. Fill me again, Spirit of Jesus.
   Fill me again, Holy Spirit of God.

3. Change my heart, Spirit of Jesus.
   Change my heart, Holy Spirit of God.

4. Bring peace to the world, Spirit of Jesus.
   Bring peace to the world, Holy Spirit of God.

16. But if we walk in the light

1 Jn 1:17

Ian Smale

With a rocky feel

But if we walk in the light as He— is in the light, we have
fel-low-ship with one a-noth - er,— and the blood of Je-sus His
Son— pu-ri - fies us from all sin.—

17. Called to a battle
(Thunder in the skies)

Mt 28:19; 1 Cor 15:54;
Eph 6:12; Rev 12:10-11

Noel & Tricia Richards

Driving

1. Called to a bat-tle, heav-en-ly war; though we may strug-gle, vic-tor-y is sure. Death will not tri-umph, though we may die; Je-sus has prom-ised our e-ter-nal life. By the

blood of the Lamb we shall ov-er-come, see the ac-cus-er
thrown down. By the word of the Lord we shall ov-er-come, raise a
vic-tor-y cry,_____ like thun-der in the skies,_____ thun-
der in the skies._____

2. Standing together, moving as one;
   We are God's army, called to overcome.
   We are commissioned, Jesus says go;
   In every nation, let His love be known.

18.   Clap your hands, all you nations
(Psalm 47)

Ian White

Joyfully

1. Clap your hands, all you na-tions, shout to God with cries of joy, O how awe-some is the Lord most high, the King ov-er all the earth.

1,2,4, To next verse

3,5

Chorus

2. He sub

Sing praise to God, sing prais-es to the King, sing prais-es to the King.

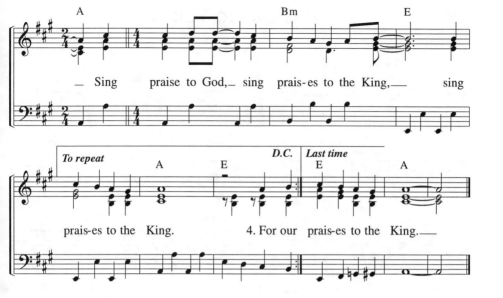

Sing praise to God,— sing prais-es to the King,— sing

prais-es to the King. 4. For our prais-es to the King.—

2. He subdued nations under us,
   The peoples under our feet,
   And He chose our inheritance for us,
   The pride of Jacob, whom He loved.

3. Now our God has ascended
   In the midst of shouts of joy,
   And the Lord is in among the trumpet sound,
   Among the trumpet sound.

   Sing praise to God,
   Sing praises to the King,
   Sing praises to the King.
   (Repeat)

4. For our God is King of all the earth,
   Sing Him a psalm of praise,
   For He rules above the nations on His throne,
   On His holy throne.

5. All the people are gathered
   Of the God of Abraham,
   For the kings of all the earth belong to God,
   And He is lifted high.

19.

Closer to You

Capo 2 (D)

Patricia Morgan

With feeling

Clo-ser to You, Lord, and clo-ser still, 'till I am whol-ly in Your will. Clo-ser to hear Your beat-ing heart, and un-der-stand what You im-part. O Breath of life come pu-ri-fy this heart of mine and sa-tis-fy. My deep de-sire is to wor-ship You, Lord of my life come clo-ser still.

20. Come, Holy Spirit

Loralee Thiessen

Come, Ho - ly Spi - rit,___ come, Ho - ly Spi -
Come, sof - ten our___ hearts,___ come, sof - ten our_

rit,___ come to___ this place,___
_ hearts,___ that we may___ o - bey,___

we will_ em - brace___ Your pre - sence.___
teach us_ Your way,___ come lead us.___

Come, Ho - ly Spi - rit.___

Come, Ho - ly Spi - rit.___

21.
Come into the heavenlies

Rev 5:12

Capo 3 (D)

Billy Funk

Building, with strength

Come in-to the heav-en-lies and sing the song the

an-gels sing, 'wor - thy, wor - thy.'

wor - thy.' 'Wor - thy is the Lamb,

wor - thy is the Lamb,

22.

Come, let us return

Deut 11:13-14; Jas 5:7

Capo 2(A)

Thoughtfully

Kevin Prosch

(Men) Come let us— re-turn— un-to— the Lord.—
(Women) Come let us— re-turn—

— un-to— the Lord.—
(Men) Come let us— re-turn— un-to— the Lord.—

(Women) Come, let us— re-turn— un-to.— (All) For He has torn us,—

but He will heal us.— For He has wound-ed us,—

23. Come, let us worship Jesus
(King of the nations)

Rev 15:4,8

Graham Kendrick

With strength

1. Come, let us wor-ship Je - sus, King of na - tions, Lord of— all. Mag - ni - fi - cent and glor-i-ous, just and mer-ci-ful. Je - sus, King of the na - tions, Je - sus, Lord of— all. Je - sus, King of the na - tions, Lord of——

all. Lord of— all. 5. Fear God and give Him glo- ry, for His hour— of judge-ment— comes. Cre- a-tor, Lord Al - migh- ty wor - ship Him a - lone.

2. Lavish our hearts' affection,
   Deepest love and highest praise.
   Voice, race and language blending
   All the world amazed.

4. Come, Lord, and fill Your temple,
   Glorify Your dwelling place,
   'Till nations see Your splendour
   And seek Your face.

3. Bring tributes from the nations,
   Come in joyful cavalcades,
   One thunderous acclamation,
   One banner raised.

5. Fear God and give Him glory,
   For His hour of judgement comes.
   Creator, Lord Almighty,
   Worship Him alone.

24.   Come, my soul, and praise the Lord.

Mt 10:31; Lk 12:7

Flowing

John Pantry

2. *(Men)* Holy, holy is the Lord, *(Women echo)*
   (Men) Who may stand before His word? *(Women echo)*
   (Men) He knows my life so well, *(Women echo)*
   (Men) Yet loves me still. *(Women echo)*

25. Deep calls to deep

Ps 42:7; 139:23

Capo 3 (D)

Robert Critchley

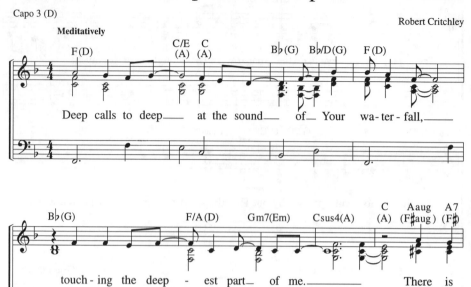

Deep calls to deep__ at the sound__ of__ Your wa-ter-fall,__

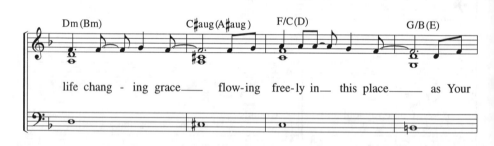

touch-ing the deep - est part__ of me._____ There is

life chang - ing grace__ flow-ing free-ly in__ this place__ as Your

deep calls to deep__ in me.__

────────── □ ▯ □ ──────────

Who may ascend the hill of the
  Lord?
Who may stand in his holy place?
He who has clean hands and a pure
  heart.

PSALM 24:3–4

────────── □ ▯ □ ──────────

26.

Don't be lazy

Heb 6:12

Capo 2 (G)

Ian Smale

With pace

Don't be la - zy, la - zy, la - zy,

la - zy, but co - py those who through faith and pa - tience re -

ceive what God has pro - mised.

27. Every time I think of You
(Never gonna stop)

Rom 8:38-39

Tim and Carla White

2. Your love never lets me down,
   Because Your love is true.
   And with Your help I know for sure
   I'll always be next to You.
   Oh, I never ever want to fall away from You,
   So there's one thing I know that I'm gonna do:

28. Faithful God

Ps 36:5

Capo 3(D)

Chris Bowater

Worshipfully and unhurried

Faith- ful God,_____ faith- ful God,_____

_ all suf - fi - cient one, I wor-ship You._____

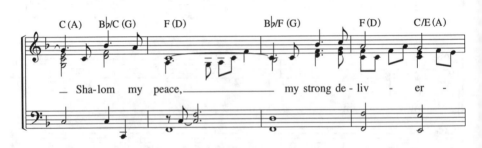

_ Sha-lom my peace,_____ my strong de - liv - er -

er, I lift You up, faith - ful God._____

— □ □ □ —

Clap your hands, all you nations;
shout to God with cries of joy.
How awesome is the Lord Most High,
the great King over all the earth!

PSALM 47:1–2

— □ □ □ —

29.

Father, I come to You
(Unending love)

Rom 5:2

Capo 2 (D)

John Barnett

Gently

1. Fa - ther, I come to— You, lift - ing up my— hands

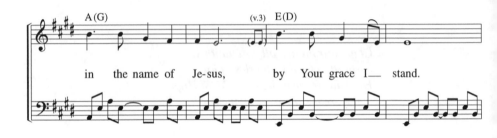

in the name of Je - sus, by Your grace I— stand.

Just be - cause— You love— me and I love Your—

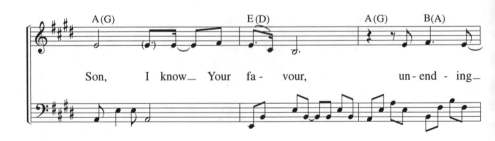

Son, I know— Your fa - vour, un - end - ing—

love. _____ Un - end - ing love,

Your ___ un - end - ing love. _____

2. I receive Your favour, Your unending love,
   Not because I've earned it, not for what I've done,
   Just because You love me and I love Your Son,
   I know Your favour, unending love.

3. It's the presence of Your kingdom as Your glory fills this place,
   And I see how much You love me as I look into Your face.
   Nothing could be better, there's nothing I would trade
   For Your favour, unending love.

30.   5000 + hungry folk

Mt 14:16-21; Mk 6:37-44;
Lk 9:13-17; Jn 6:5-13
Ian Smale

2. The 6 x 2 said O O O,
   The 6 x 2 said O O O,
   The 6 x 2 said O O O,
   Where can I get some food from?

3. Just 1 had 1 2 3 4 5,
   Just 1 had 1 2 3 4 5,
   Just 1 had 1 2 3 4 5
   Loaves and 1 2 fishes.

4. When Jesus blessed the 5 + 2,
   When Jesus blessed the 5 + 2,
   When Jesus blessed the 5 + 2
   They were increased many x over.

5. 5 0 0 0 + 8 it up,
   5 0 0 0 + 8 it up,
   5 0 0 0 + 8 it up,
   With 1 2 3 4 5 6 7 8 9 10 11 12 basketfuls left over.

31.

Focus my eyes

Jn 4:23-24

Ian White

Gently

1. Fo-cus my eyes on You, O Lord, fo-cus my eyes on You; to

wor-ship in spi-rit and in truth, fo-cus my eyes on You.

2. Turn round my life to You, O Lord,
   Turn round my life to You;
   To know from this night You've made me new,
   Turn round my life to You.

3. Fill up my heart with praise, O Lord,
   Fill up my heart with praise;
   To speak of Your love in every place,
   Fill up my heart with praise.

32. For the sake of the multitudes

(We hear the cry of the cities)

1 Pet 2:25

Lex Loizides

Resolutely, not too fast

For the sake of_ the mul-ti-tudes, in the pow-er_ of Je-sus Christ, we are ea-ger_ to preach the truth, and to wil-ling-ly give our lives. And we know_ the Shep-herd of our souls_ _ is march-ing on,_ and by His grace we're fol-low-ing_ His call.

We hear the cry of the ci-ties, we will lift our
hearts to God; called and sent__ in His won-der-ful love,__ and
soul by soul es-tab - lish-ing the king-dom of God._____

—□ □ □—

God has ascended amid shouts of
joy,
the Lord amid the sounding of
trumpets.
Sing praises to God, sing praises;
sing praises to our King, sing
praises.
For God is the King of all the earth;
sing to him a psalm of praise.

PSALM 47:5–7

—□ □ □—

33.

From Your throne, O Lord

Lively

Christopher Cartwright

1. From Your throne, O Lord, let Your fire_ fall_ up-on us; let us feel the touch of the Spi-rit in_ our hearts. To e-quip us and_ em-pow'r us, send us out to heal_ the land, in Your name to shine___ the light of Christ.

2. From the Father's heart send us waves of Your compassion;
Move us, Lord, to pray for Your will to come on earth.
Interceding for a nation that is dying, lost and blind,
Let us see them with the eyes of Christ.

3. Lord, we lift one voice in a song of joy and triumph;
Let Your word rise up from our lips, that in our lives
We will let the world know Jesus is the Victor and the King,
Let our anthem ring throughout the land.

34.

Give your thanks

Brightly

Dave Bilbrough

35. Glorify

Linda Barnhill

With strength

1. Glo - ri-fy_____ Your name.__ Glo - ri-fy_

_____ Your name.__ Raise the ban-

-ner,___ raise_ it high.__ Fa - ther, glo-ri-fy._

2. Jesus, light the flame.
   Jesus, light the flame.
   Give us passion for Your name,
   Jesus, light the flame.

3. Purify Your bride.
   Purify Your bride.
   Cleanse her with Your holy fire,
   Jesus, purify.

———— □ ☐ □ ————

O Lord, open my lips,
*   and my mouth will declare your*
*   praise.*
You do not delight in sacrifice, or I
*   would bring it;*
*   you do not take pleasure in burnt*
*   offerings.*
The sacrifices of God are a broken
*   spirit;*
*   a broken and contrite heart,*
*   O God, you will not despise.*

PSALM 51:15–17

———— □ ☐ □ ————

36.

God is so good

Ps 68:5; 104:3-4; Rom 1:20

Kevin Prosch

Steadily, with awe

(And) God _____ is so good. _____

(And) God _____ is so good. _____

1. 2. He rides_ up - on __ the wings of the
3. You reign_ on high_ in ma - jes -

wind, He is_ ex - alt - ed _____ by His_ name Jah_
ty, (and) the wi - dow's heart_____ cau - ses_ to sing_

He walks_in the midst _ of the stones_of fire,_
You hear_the _ cry _ of the fa - ther -less,_

37.

God of heaven
(Heart of a lover)

Deut 29:12; Song 2:16;
Is 49:15; 53:3; 66:13;
Rev 1:8; 17:14; 19:16
Stuart Townend

Capo 2(D)

Steadily

1. God of heav'n,_ with the heart _ of a lov-er;_ conqu'ring King,_ with com-pas-sion in _ His voice._ Sov'-reign Lord,_ with the care of a mo-ther;_ to You we bring_ our_ lives, _ know-ing You will take_ us _ in. _ So let's be pure and ho-

2. Jesus Christ, You're the Alpha and Omega;
   King of kings, who laid aside His crown.
   Man of woes, but a Friend to the friendless;
   To You we bring our fears, knowing You will set us free.

38. God, our God, blesses us

Ps 67:5-7

Rosie Fellingham

God, our God, bless - ses us, God bless - ses us, that all the ends of the earth may fear Him. fear Him. Let all the peo - ples praise Thee, O God,

39.
God, You are an awesome God
(Awesome God)

Charlotte Exon
& Andy Thorpe

Steadily

God, You are an awe - some God, and your do - min - ion reach-es to the

hea - vens, and all na - tions sing Your praise; as Your

peo-ple, we de-clare— Your ho - li - ness.— Ho - ly, ho - ly,

ho-ly is the Lord. Ho - ly, ho - ly, ho-ly is the Lord.

40.

Goliath

1 Sam 17:4-51

Keith Currie

Chorus strongly, verses smoothly

2. David heard him brag,
   Put five stones into his bag.
   Ran to fight, his face defiant,
   He would face the giant.

3. "Am I a dog?" Goliath asked,
   "That you'd choose rocks to perform your task?
   Would you like to be bird feed?
   I'll make you the seed."

4. David said, with twirling sling,
   "You forget one little thing:
   Battles aren't won with spears and swords,
   The battle is the Lord's."

5. One smooth stone from a little creek bed
   Hit Goliath in the head:
   There was no more giant to dread -
   Goliath now was dead.

41.

Go to all nations

Mt 28:18-20; Rev 22:20

Joyfully

Bryn Haworth

42.

Great is the darkness
(Come, Lord Jesus)

Is 65:19; Joel 2:29; Mt 28:19;
Acts 2:18; 2 Pet 3:12; Rev 22:20

Noel Richards/Gerald Coates

1. Great is the dark-ness that cov-ers the earth, op-pres-sion, in-jus-tice and pain. Na-tions are slip-ping in hope-less des-pair, though ma-ny have come in Your name. Watch-ing while sa-ni-ty dies, touched by the mad-ness and lies.

Chorus

Come Lord Je-sus, come Lord Je-sus, pour out Your Spi-rit we pray. Come Lord Je-sus, come Lord Je-sus, pour out Your Spi-rit on us to-day.

2. May now Your church rise with power and love,
   This glorious gospel proclaim.
   In every nation salvation will come
   To those who believe in Your name.
   Help us bring light to this world
   That we might speed Your return.

3. Great celebrations on that final day
   When out of the heavens You come.
   Darkness will vanish, all sorrow will end,
   And rulers will bow at Your throne.
   Our great commission complete,
   Then face to face we shall meet.

43. Hang on

Acts 1:4; Eph 6:13; Phil 3:12

Richard Hubbard

1. Hang on, stand still, stay put, hold tight; wait for the Spi - rit of God. ___ Don't push, don't shove, don't move, that's right; just wait for the Spi - rit of God. ___ Hang ___ For you will re - ceive ___ the

2. Let go, launch out, press on, don't fight;
   Be filled with the Spirit of God.
   Move on, make way, step out, that's right;
   Be filled with the Spirit of God.
   Let go, launch out, press on, don't fight;
   Be filled with the Spirit of God.
   Move on, make way, step out, that's right;
   Be filled with the Spirit of God.

   For You have received the power of God,
   You have received the power of God,
   You have received the power of God
   Now the Holy Spirit lives within you.

44. Have you got an appetite?

Ps 34:8; Jn 6:57;
Heb 5:13-14

Mick Gisbey

Steadily

1. Have you got an ap-pe - tite? Do you eat what is right? Are you feed-ing on the word — of — God? Are you fat or are you thin? Are you real-ly full with-in? Do you find your strength in Him or are you star-ving?

Chorus

You and me all should be ex-er-cis-ing

46.

He has risen

Ps 16:10; Mt 28:6; Mk 16:6; Lk 24:6;
Acts 2:27; 1 Cor 13:12; 15:13-20; 1 Thess 4:16

Capo 2 (D)

Gerald Coates, Noel Richards
and Tricia Richards

Brightly ♩ = 137

He has— ri-sen, He has— ri-sen,

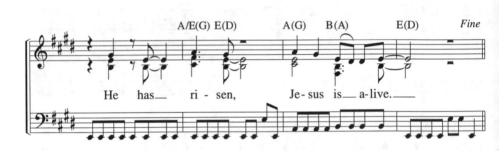

He has— ri-sen, Je-sus is— a-live.—

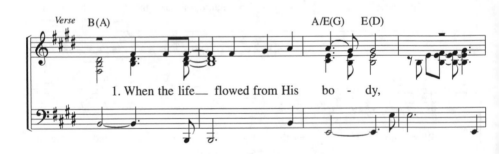

1. When the life— flowed from His bo-dy,

seemed like Je-sus' mis-sion failed.—

But His sa - cri - fice ac - com - plished,

vic - t'ry ov - er sin and hell.___

2. In the grave God did not leave Him,
   For His body to decay;
   Raised to life, the great awakening,
   Satan's power He overcame.

3. If there were no resurrection,
   We ourselves could not be raised;
   But the Son of God is living,
   So our hope is not in vain.

4. When the Lord rides out of heaven,
   Mighty angels at His side,
   They will sound the final trumpet,
   From the grave we shall arise.

5. He has given life immortal,
   We shall see Him face to face;
   Through eternity we'll praise Him,
   Christ, the champion of our faith.

47.

He is lovely

Bob Fitts

(* or "You are lovely")

48.
He is the Lord
Gen 1:3; Ex 15:11; Joel 2:32; Rom 10:13
(Show Your power)

Kevin Prosch

2. Your gospel, O Lord, is the hope for our nation;
   You are the Lord.
   It's the power of God for our salvation.
   You are the Lord.
   We ask not for riches, but look to the cross;
   You are the Lord.
   And for our inheritance give us the lost.
   You are the Lord.

49.

He made the earth
(Our God)

Ps 8:3-5

Gill Broomhall

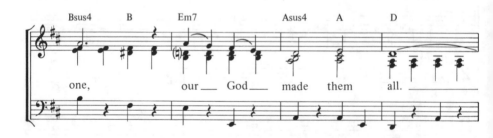

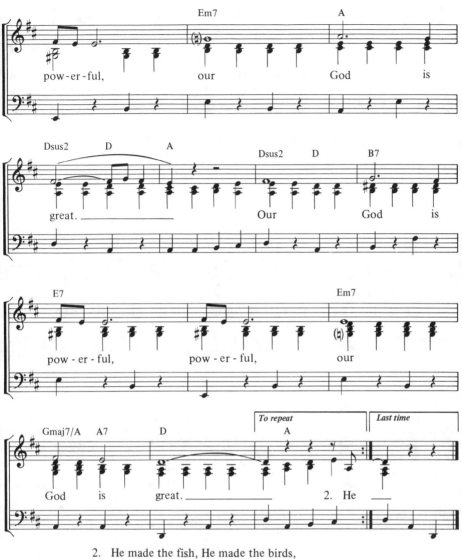

2. He made the fish, He made the birds,
   Elephants and worms, creeping things that squirm.
   Mice so small, giraffes so tall;
   Our God made them all.
   Our God is wonderful, wonderful,
   Our God is great.
   Our God is wonderful, wonderful,
   Our God is great.

3. He made the boys, He made the girls,
   He made our mums and dads, to teach us good from bad.
   He cares for me, He cares for you;
   Our God loves us all.
   Our God is beautiful, beautiful,
   Our God is great.
   Our God is beautiful, beautiful,
   Our God is great.

50. He reigns

Mt 28:9; Mk 11:9; Col 2:15

Capo 3 (D)

Rick Ridings

Driving

He reigns, He reigns, Je-sus reigns,— He reigns en-throned— in ma-jes-ty.— Shout your praise,— His ban-ners raise,— for Je-sus— reigns.— Shout ho-san - na, Je - sus reigns.— 1. Our high-est praise— we bring—

to our great e-ter - nal King._____ His glo-ry fills__ the skies,_

_____ now from   earth let praise__ a - rise._____ He

2. He spoiled the hosts of hell,
   And like blazing stars, they fell.
   He led them forth in chains
   Now our mighty Victor reigns!

51. Holiness is Your life in me
(Only the Blood)

Rom 3:25; 1 Jn 1:7

Brian Doerksen

Expressively

Ho-li-ness___ is Your life in me, ___ mak-ing me clean through Your blood._

___ Ho-li-ness___ is Your fire in me,___

purg-ing my heart___ like a flood.___ I know___

You are___ per - fect in ho - li - ness.

Your life___ in me,___ set - ting me free,___

52. Holy Ghost

Joel 2:30; Jn 3:8; Acts 2:19

Bjorn Aslaksen

Steadily, but with anticipation
Chorus

Ho - ly Ghost,___ You won-der-ful Ho - ly Ghost,___ ___ a wind blow-ing strong,_____ blow-ing from hea - ven.___

We have de-ci-ded to go_____ all the way_ with our God._

Re - vi- val in_ the land, that's our goal;_____ as

sol - diers in_ His ar - my__ we'll fight with heart_ and soul. _

(Final chorus)
Blood and fire, we call upon blood and fire,
A wind blowing strong, blowing from heaven.
Blood and fire, we call upon blood and fire,
A wind blowing strong, blowing from heaven.

53.

Holy, holy, holy is the Lord

(In His eyes)

Rev 4:8; 5:12

Bryn Haworth

pre - cious   in   God's   sight,   so

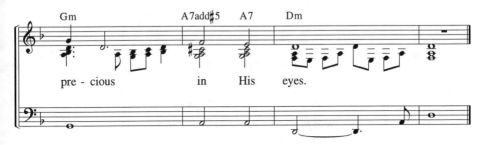

pre - cious   in   His   eyes.

2. Worthy, worthy, worthy is the Lamb.
   Worthy, worthy, worthy is the Lamb.

3. Glory, I give glory to the Lamb of God.
   Glory, I give glory to the Lamb of God.

——————— □ ▢ □ ———————

I will praise you, O Lord my God,
with all my heart;
I will glorify your name for ever.
For great is your love towards me;
you have delivered my soul from
the depths of the grave.

PSALM 86:12–13

——————— □ ▢ □ ———————

54.
Holy is Your name

Ps 16:5; 18:30; Gal 2:20;
Phil 4:19; Rev 15:3

John Paculabo

Steadily

1.3. Ho - ly is Your name, Ye - shu - a, my de -
2. Per - fect are Your ways, Je - ho - vah, my —

liv-er-er. Wor - thy of all praise, You ev - er - liv-ing
Fa - ther. Faith - ful is Your love, You gave Your-self for

God. / me. In — You — I have se - cur-i-ty; in —

You — I put my trust. In — You I have con-fi-dence, You

meet my ev - 'ry need.

55.
Holy One

Ps 16:5; 1 Cor 6:11

Mick Gisbey

Steadily, building to the chorus

Holy One,___ my life is in Your hand; my song an off'ring of my heart, re-deemed, washed clean, by faith I stand se-cure. In You Jesus I live. To You the glo-ry, to You the pow-er,

56. Holy Spirit

Suzi de Faye

(Format: sing the song through, adding each time one numbered section, beginning with "Pour Your power")

57.
Holy Spirit, move within me

Charlotte Exon

With feeling

Ho - ly Spi - rit, move with - in me, Ho - ly Spi - rit, come u - pon me now. Ho - ly Spi - rit, lead me to the se - cret place of prayer, ma - ni - fest the glo - ry of God.

Ho - ly Spi - rit, You are wel-come, Ho - ly Spi - rit, we de - sire You.

Ho - ly Spi - rit, wor - ship through us, let us see the glo-ry of God.

Sing to the Lord a new song;
   sing to the Lord, all the earth.
Sing to the Lord, praise his name;
   proclaim his salvation day after
      day.
Declare his glory among the nations,
   his marvellous deeds among all
      peoples.

PSALM 96:1–3

58.   How sweet the name of Jesus sounds

Ex 6:15; Is 65:19; Joel 2:32; Jn 6:58;
Acts 4:12; Rom 10:13; Heb 12:2

Music: Chris Bowater
Words: John Newton (adapted by C. Bowater)

1. How sweet the name of Je-sus sounds in a be-lie-ver's ear; it soothes his sor-rows, heals his wounds, and drives a-way his fear. 2. It makes the woun-ded spi-rit whole,

3. Dear name, the Rock on which I build,
   My shield, and hiding place;
   My never-failing treasury, filled
   With boundless stores of grace.

4. Jesus, my Shepherd, Saviour, Friend,
   My Prophet, Priest, and King;
   My Lord, my Life, my Way, my End,
   Accept the praise I bring.
   Accept the praise I bring.

5. Weak is the effort of my heart,
   And cold my warmest thought;
   But when I see You as You are,
   I'll praise You as I ought.

6. I would Your boundless love proclaim
   With every fleeting breath;
   So shall the music of Your name
   Refresh my soul in death.
   Refresh my soul in death.

59.

How wonderful

Rom 5:5; 2 Cor 5:19

Dave Bilbrough

As a jig

How— won-der-ful,— how— glo-ri-ous— is— the love of— God,— bring-ing— heal-ing,— for-give - ness,— won-der-ful love. 1. Let cel - e-bra-tion— ech-o through— this— land;— we bring re - con-ci-li-a-

- tion,— we bring hope——— to ev - 'ry man.——— How—

2. We proclaim the kingdom
   Of our God is here;
   Come and join the heavenly anthem
   Ringing loud and ringing clear:

3. Listen to the music
   As His praises fill the air;
   With joy and with gladness
   Tell the people everywhere:

60.   I believe there is a God in heaven

Is 53:5; Jn 3:14; 19:30;
Col 1:20; Heb 7:27

Dave Bilbrough

I be-lieve there is a God in heav'n who paid the price for all my sin; shed His blood to o-pen up the way for me to walk with Him. Gave His life up-on a cross, took the pun-ish-ment for us, of-fered up Him-self in love, Je- sus,

Je - sus. "It is fin - ished" was His cry; not

ev - en death could now de - ny. The Son of God ex - alt - ed

high, Je - sus, Je - sus, Je - sus.

61. I bow down

Heb 7:17,25; 1 Jn 1:7

With feeling

David Fellingham

I bow down___ in hum-ble a-dor - a - tion,___ speak Your name___ ___ with love and de - vo - tion,___ Je - sus, the Lamb sa-cri-ficed for me. I see Your face,___ Your ten-der hands___ scarred for me. I fall at Your feet___ with songs of prais- es sing - ing;___ my joy is com-plete.___ You ful-fil my long - ing.__ Pro - phet of

— □ ▢ □ —

Ascribe to the Lord the glory due to
his name;
bring an offering and come into
his courts.
Worship the Lord in the splendour
of his holiness;
tremble before him, all the earth.

PSALM 96:8–9

— □ ▢ □ —

62. I delight in You, Lord

Is 61:10

David Baroni

Flowing

I de-light— in You, Lord.— I de-light— in Your pre-sence. There's no-thing as sweet as to sit at Your feet, no-thing that I'd— ra-ther do than de-light my-self, I de-light my-self in You.— I de-

63.

I know a place
(At the cross)

1 Cor 15:3; Col 2:14; 1 Pet 3:18

Capo 2 (D)

Flowing

Randy & Terry Butler

I know a place, a wonderful place, where ac-cused and con-demned find mer-cy and grace. Where the wrongs we have done and the wrongs done to us were

64. I love You, Lord, my strength

(Youre my stronghold)

Ps 18:1-2, 7, 15-17

Phil Lawson Johnston

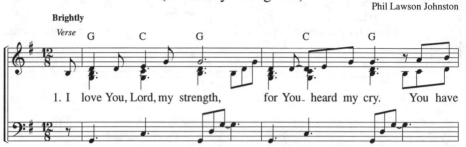

1. I love You, Lord, my strength, for You heard my cry. You have

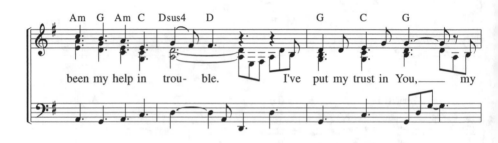

been my help in trou- ble. I've put my trust in You, my

ref- uge and my hope, You're the Rock on which I

stand. You're my strong - hold, You're my

2. I love You, Lord, my strength,
   You reached down from on high,
   And You rescued me from trouble.
   You've taken hold of me,
   And set me on a rock,
   And now this is where I stand.

3. I love You, Lord, my strength,
   There is no other rock,
   And now I will not be shaken.
   The sea may roar and crash,
   The mountains quake and fall,
   Ah, but on this Rock I stand.

65. I'm looking up to Jesus

Ian Smale

I'm look-ing up to Je-sus, ___ His face is shin-ing beau-ty. ___
___ I'm feel-ing so un-wor-thy, ___ yet His Spi-rit leads me on.
I'm look-ing up to Je-sus, ___ His ra-di-ance sur-rounds me. ___
___ I feel so pure and clean, a taste of
heav-en on ___ earth. I'm look-ing up to Je-sus. ___

Shout for joy to the Lord, all the
     earth.
Serve the Lord with gladness;
come before him with joyful songs.

PSALM 100:1–2

66.
I'm standing here to testify
(Come to the light)

Joel 2:25; Ps 100:5; 106:1; 107:1; 118:1,29;135:3; 136:1; Mt 11:19; Lk 7:34; Jn 15:15; Jas 2:23; 4:8

With a steady rhythm

Kevin Prosch

Verse

G · C · G

(Leader) I'm stand-ing here_ to tes - ti - fy, (All) O, the Lord is good. (Leader) to
did not think_ I could have peace,

D · G

sing of how_ He changed_ my heart. (All) O, the Lord is good.
trapped in-side_ by fear_ and shame. (Leader) He

C · G

(Leader) I was bound_ by hate and pride, (All) O, the Lord is good, (Leader)
wiped a - way_ all of my grief, when

D · G · **1, 3.**

nev - er know - ing of_ His light. (All) O, the Lord is good (Leader) I
I be - lieved_ up - on_ His name.

2, 4. *Chorus*

C · G

(All) Come to the light,____ come as you are;____ you can be_

67. In every circumstance

Neh 8:10; Eph 1:18-19

David Fellingham

With a 12/8 feel

In ev-'ry cir - cum-stance of life___ You are with me,

glor ious Fa - ther. And I have put___ my trust___ in You,___

___ that I may know the glor - i - ous hope___

___ to which I'm called.___

68.

In mystery reigning

John Pantry

With a gentle lilt

1. In mys-ter-y reign-ing, King ov-er all,
hear an-gels pro-claim-ing, Je-sus is Lord.
To each gen-er-a-tion Your love is the same,
won-der-ful Sav-iour, we wor-ship Your name.

2. A beauty that's timeless, who can compare?
All earth stands in silence, when You appear.
Your kingdom is boundless, Your love without end;
Wonder of wonders, this King is my friend!

3. All power has been given into Your hands.
Through blood and by suffering You now command.
And no opposition can stand in Your light.
Crowned King of heaven, we kneel at the sight.

69.

In these days of darkness
(Carry the fire)

Is 6:8

With conviction

Sue Rinaldi & Steve Bassett

1. In these days of dark - ness, who will bear the light?_ In all of this_ con-fu - sion, who will rage a-gainst_ the night? And who will light a bea - con in the face of this dark,_ dark sky?_ With a hope that is e-ter - nal, with a

I will not rest, I will not tire, with

all my strength I'll car-ry the fire._____

2. Where there is oppression,
   Who will raise the flame?
   For the sake of all the children,
   Who will touch the fields of shame?
   And who will light a beacon
   In the face of this dark, dark sky,
   With a hope that is eternal,
   With a love that will never die?

3. Who will burn with passion,
   Blazing from the heart,
   To forge a new tomorrow?
   We must tell the world
   Of a hope that is eternal,
   Of a love that will never die.
   And we will light a beacon
   In the face of this dark, dark sky.

70.

Into the darkness
(Come, Lord Jesus, come)

Is 7:14; 9:2; Mt 1:23;
Phil 2:9; Rev 22:20

Maggi Dawn

Into the darkness
of this world, in-to the sha - dows of the night; in-to this love-less place
You came, light-ened our bur - dens, eased our pain, and
made these hearts Your home. In-to the dark - ness once
a-gain, O come, Lord Je-sus, come. Come with Your love

_ to make _ us whole, _ come with Your light _ to lead _ us on, _ driv-ing the dark - ness far from our souls: _ O come, Lord Je-sus, come. _

2. Into the longing of our souls,
   Into these heavy hearts of stone,
   Shine on us now Your piercing light,
   Order our lives and souls aright,
   By grace and love unknown,
   Until in You our hearts unite,
   O come, Lord Jesus, come.

3. O Holy Child, Emmanuel,
   Hope of the ages, God with us,
   Visit again this broken place,
   Till all the earth declares Your praise
   And Your great mercies own.
   Now let Your love be born in us,
   O come, Lord Jesus, come.

(Last Chorus)

Come in Your glory, take Your place,
Jesus, the Name above all names,
We long to see You face to face,
O come, Lord Jesus, come.

71. I sing a simple song of love

(Arms of love)

Craig Musseau

Gently, with feeling

—————————— □ ▢ □ ——————————

*Enter his gates with thanksgiving
and his courts with praise;
give thanks to him and praise his
name.*

PSALM 100:4

—————————— □ ▢ □ ——————————

72.

I sing praises

1 Chron 16:25; Ps 48:1; 96:4; 145:3

Terry MacAlmon

2. I give glory to Your name...

73.

Slow 4

I stand amazed
(Father, I love You)

Ps 103:11-12; Song 1:2; 4:10;
Rom 8:39

Paul Oakley

Verse

I stand a-mazed— when I re-a-lize Your love for me— is be-yond all mea-sure. Lord, I can't de-ny— Your love for me is— great.

Chorus

It's as— high, high as— the hea-vens— a-bove,— such is— the depth of— Your love— to-ward those who fear— You. Oh— Lord, far as— the east is— from—

74. It is good to give thanks to the Lord

Ps 106:1,6-7,14,43-44,48
John Bell & Graham Maule

2. Our sin is the sin of our fathers,
   We have done wrong, we all have been evil;
   Like those who once lived in bondage,
   We paid no heed to all You had done.

3. Our fathers forsook Your love,
   At the Red Sea they questioned their God;
   They fell from their faith in the desert,
   And put God to the test in the wilderness.

4. Time after time He would rescue them,
   Yet in malice they dared to defy Him;
   Despite this He came to their aid
   When He heard their cries of distress.

5. Save us, O Lord, in Your love;
   Bring us back from all that offends You.
   Look not alone at our sins,
   But remember Your promise of mercy.

6. Blessed be the Lord God of Israel
   Both now and through all eternity;
   Let nations and people cry out
   And sing Amen! Alleluia!

———— □ ▢ □ ————

The Lord is good and his love endures
for ever;
his faithfulness continues through
all generations.

PSALM 100:5

———— □ ▢ □ ————

75. It is the cry of my heart

(Cry of my heart)

Ps 86:11

Terry Butler

It is the cry of my heart to fol-low You. It is the cry of my heart to be close_ to You. It is the cry of my heart to fol-low all of the days_ of my life._

1. Teach me Your ho-ly ways,_ O Lord,_

2. Open my eyes so I can see
   The wonderful things that You do.
   Open my heart up more and more
   And make it wholly devoted to You.

76. I've got the life of God in me

Rom 5:5
Author unknown
Arr. Stuart Townend

Capo 3 (D)

2. I've got the word of God in me.
   I've got the word of God in me.
   I've got His word, His nature and His ability,
   I've got the word of God in me.

3. I've got the joy of God in me.
   I've got the joy of God in me.
   I've got His joy, His nature and His ability,
   I've got the joy of God in me.

4. I've got the love of God in me.
   I've got the love of God in me.
   I've got His love, His nature and His ability,
   I've got the love of God in me.

— □ ▢ □ —

Praise the Lord, O my soul;
all my inmost being, praise his
holy name.
Praise the Lord, O my soul,
and forget not all his benefits.

PSALM 103:1–2

— □ ▢ □ —

77. I waited patiently
(Many will see)

Capo 3 (D)

Ps 40: 1-5

Ian White

1. I wait-ed pa-tient-ly— for the Lord,— He turned and heard— my cry. He lift-ed me from the pit,— out from the mud and mire. He put my feet on a rock, and gave me a firm place to stand. He put a new— song in my— mouth, a hymn of praise to God,—— a hymn of praise—— to God.—

2. Blessed is the man who trusts the Lord,
And turns from all the proud;
From all those who have turned aside,
To follow what is false.
Many are the wonders that You have done,
All the things You have planned;
Were I to count they still would be
Too many to declare,
Too many to declare.

78.

I was made to praise You

Eph 5:20; 1 Thess 5:18

Chris Christensen

Gently, with feeling

1. I was made to praise You, I was made to glo-ri-fy Your name, in ev-'ry cir-cum-stance, to find a chance to thank You. I was made to love You, I was made to wor-ship at Your feet, and to o-bey You, I was made for You.

2. I will always praise You,
   I will always glorify Your name,
   In every circumstance
   To find a chance to thank You.
   I will always love You,
   I will always worship at Your feet,
   And I'll obey You Lord,
   I was made for You.

―――――― □ ☐ □ ――――――

Praise the Lord, you his angels,
you mighty ones who do his
bidding,
who obey his word.
Praise the Lord, all his heavenly
hosts,
you his servants who do his will.
Praise the Lord, all his works
everywhere in his dominion.

PSALM 103:20–22

―――――― □ ☐ □ ――――――

79.

I will be Yours
(Eternity)

Is 65:19

Gently flowing

Brian Doerkson

I will be Yours,— You will be mine—— to-geth - er in e-ter-ni-ty.—

— Our hearts of love— will be en - twined,—— to-geth-

er in e-ter-ni-ty,— for ev - er in e-ter-ni-ty.——

No— more tears of pain— in our eyes;—

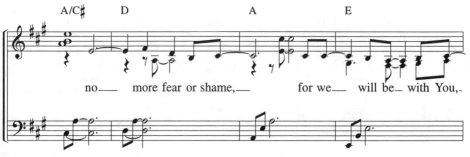

no— more fear or shame,— for we— will be— with You,-

— for we— will be—with You.——

80. I will extol the Lord
(Holy and awesome)

Capo 2(A)

Ps 145: 1-2; Prov 1:7; 9:10

Steadily ♩ = 78

Ian White

81. I will give thanks to the Lord *Ps 7:17; 32:7; Heb 13:8*
(O Most High)

Mark Altrogge

Moderately

Verse

I will— give thanks— to— the Lord— with all— my heart,—
I will— be glad— and— ex-alt— in You,— my Lord,—

— I will sing glo-ri— ous prais— es to Your
— yes-ter-day, to-day, for ev— er, You're the

1. name;_____
2. same._____

Chorus O Most High,—

You who are— my strong-hold,— when troub-les come,—

82.

I will praise You
(Psalm 138)

Ps 138: 1-3,8

Bryn Haworth

1. I will praise You, O Lord, with all of my heart. I will praise You, O Lord, with all of my heart. Be-fore the gods I will sing Your

2. You have exalted above all things
   Your name and Your word.
   You have exalted above all things
   Your name and Your word.
   I called to You, and You answered me.
   When I called to You, You made me strong.

——————————— □ ▢ □ ———————————

I will extol the Lord with all my heart
in the council of the upright and
in the assembly.

PSALM 111:1

——————————— □ ▢ □ ———————————

83.
I will praise you with the harp
(O Holy One of Israel)

Ps 71:22-24

Capo 2 (D)

Ian White

2. Those who want to harm me
   Are put to shame and confused.
   I will sing my praise to You
   With the lyre, with the lyre.

84.

I will wait

Ps 22:2; 42:8; 59:16; 77:6; 91:5;
Is 8:17; Lam 3:24-26

Meditatively

Maggi Dawn

I will___ wait for Your peace___ to come__ to me.___ I will___

wait for Your peace___ to come__ to me,___ and I'll sing___ in the dark-

ness,___ and I'll wait with-out fear,___ and I'll sing___ in the dark-

ness,___ and I'll wait with - out fear.___

Praise the Lord.

Blessed is the man who fears the Lord,
  who finds great delight in his
  commands.

PSALM 112

85.

I will wave my hands

Ian Smale

I will wave my hands in praise and a-dor-a-tion, I will wave my hands in praise and a-dor-a-tion, I will wave my hands in praise and a-dor-a-tion, praise and a-dor-a-tion to the liv-ing God. For He's giv-en me hands that just love clap-ping; one, two, one, two, three, and He's

86. I worship You, O Lord
(Lord over all)

Jn 4:24

Callie Gerbrandt

87.

Jesus

Phil 2:9-11

Andy Thorpe

With feeling

Je - sus, —— (Je - sus, ——) Je - sus, —— (Je - sus, —) it's the Name —— a - bove all names. And at the name of Je - sus ev-'ry knee shall bow, —— and ev-'ry tongue con - fess He is Lord.

88.

Jesus

Mt 11:19; Lk 7:34; Jn 1:14; 4:8; Phil 2:9

(Friend of sinners)

Gently

Bryn Haworth

1. Je - sus, Je - sus, Son of
2. Je - sus, Je - sus, Light of

God, Son of__ man, friend of sin - ners,
life, Lord of__ all,

gift of__ God. full of grace and truth.

You have come__ to__ us, Your

pre - sence__ has filled this__ place.   We will

draw near__ to__You,   we   come, Lord,__to seek Your   face,

3. Jesus, Jesus,
   My heart aches, my soul waits,
   For Your healing, Lord, I pray.

4. Jesus, Jesus,
   Mighty God, holy Child,
   Name above all names.

   (Chorus)

5. Jesus, Jesus,
   Son of God, Son of man,
   My soul thirsts for You.

89.

Jesus, forgive me

Martin Lore

With energy

Verse

1. Je-sus, for-give me. Je-sus, free me. Je-sus, touch me. Je-sus, fill me.

Chorus

I lift my head,— lift my heart,— lift my soul— to— You. I give my life,— give my-self,— give it all— to— You.

2. Jesus, teach me.
Jesus, lead me.
Jesus, guide me.
Jesus, use me.

———————— □ ▢ □ ————————

Let the name of the Lord be praised
both now and for evermore.
From the rising of the sun to the
place where it sets
the name of the Lord is to be
praised.

PSALM 113:2–3

———————— □ ▢ □ ————————

90.

Jesus, I am thirsty
(More of You)

Capo 3 (D)

Jn 4:14

Don Harris & Martin J Nystrom

Je-sus, I am thirs-ty, won't You come and fill___ me?

Earth-ly things have left me dry,___ on-ly You can sa-tis-fy,___

all I want is more___ of You. All I want is more of You,-

___ all I want is more of You;___ no-thing I de-sire,___ Lord,-

but more of You._____ All I want is _____

more of You._____

91. Jesus is the name we honour
(Jesus is our God)

Phil 2:9-10; Heb 1:3

Phil Lawson Johnston

1. Je - sus is the name we ho - nour; Je - sus is the name we praise. Ma-jes - tic Name a - bove all oth - er names, the high - est heav'n and earth pro - claim that Je - sus is our God. We will

2. Jesus is the name we worship;
   Jesus is the name we trust.
   He is the King above all other kings,
   Let all creation stand and sing
   That Jesus is our God.

3. Jesus is the Father's splendour;
   Jesus is the Father's joy.
   He will return to reign in majesty,
   And every eye at last will see
   That Jesus is our God.

92.
Jesus, restore to us again

Mt 5:17; 17:4; Mk 9:5;
Lk 9:33; 24:44; Jn 1:14; 16:13;
Eph 6:17; 1 Thess 1:5; Rev 19:13

Graham Kendrick

Flowing

1. Je-sus, re - store to us a - gain the gos-pel of Your ho-ly name, that comes with pow'r, not words a - lone, owned, signed and sealed from heav-en's throne. Spi-rit and word in one a - greed; the pro-mise to the pow-er wed.___ The word is near, here in our mouths and

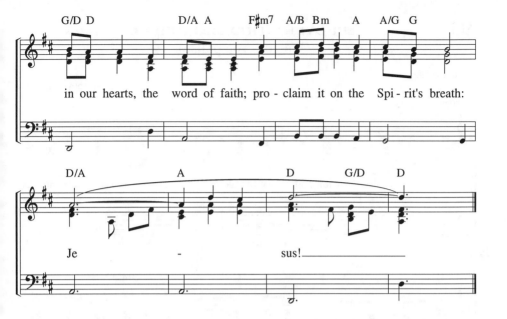

in our hearts, the word of faith; pro - claim it on the Spi - rit's breath:

Je - sus!

2. Your word, O Lord, eternal stands,
   Fixed and unchanging in the heavens.
   The Word made flesh, to earth come down
   To heal our world with nail-pierced hands.
   Among us here You lived and breathed,
   You are the message we received.

3. Spirit of truth, lead us, we pray
   Into all truth as we obey.
   And as God's will we gladly choose,
   Your ancient powers again will prove
   Christ's teaching truly comes from God,
   He is indeed the living Word.

4. Upon the heights of this great land
   With Moses and Elijah stand.
   Reveal Your glory once again,
   Show us Your face, declare Your name.
   Prophets and law, in You complete
   Where promises and power meet.

5. Grant us in this decisive hour
   To know the Scriptures and the power;
   The knowledge in experience proved,
   The power that moves and works by love.
   May word and works join hands as one,
   The word go forth, the Spirit come.

93.
Let every tribe and tongue
(We give You praise)

Ex 3:14; Rev 5:9-10,12

With strength

Debbye Graafsma

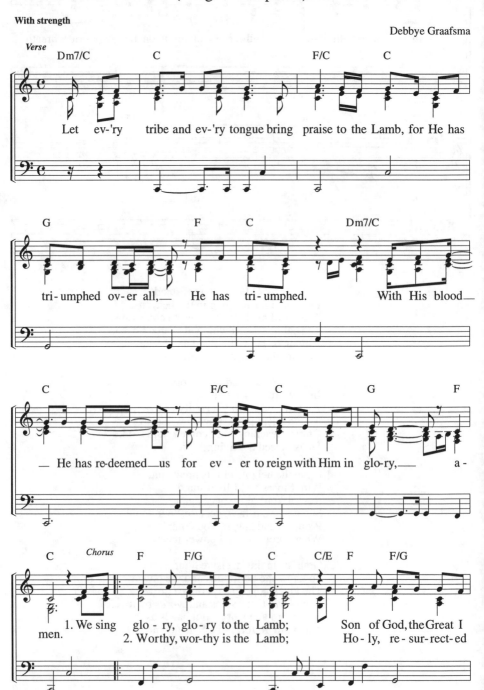

94.

Let's join together

Dave Bilbrough

With a light rhythmic feel

1. Let's join_ to-geth - er,_ lift up our hearts_ as one;_
let's pro-claim_ His might - y name,_ for He has ov - er-come_
_ all that stands_ be-fore_ Him_ by the pow-er of_ His blood,-
_ sing to Je-sus_ the Sav - iour,_ He's the Lord of heav'n_ a-bove._

2. He reigns forever,
   He is the King of kings,
   Our Saviour and Deliverer,
   The reason that we sing.
   His grace is like a fountain,
   A never ending stream;
   Let's celebrate together,
   And let His praise begin.

3. Dance now before Him,
   Proclaim His victory;
   Hail Him as the Saviour
   Who's come to set men free.
   His word will stand forever,
   For all authority
   Has been given to Jesus
   Through all eternity.

95.

Let the righteous sing

Ps 68:3-6

Bryn Haworth

Capo 3 (D)

Bright and rhythmic

Let the right - eous sing, come let the right - eous dance, re -
Shout for joy— to God who rides up - on— the clouds, how

joice be - fore— your God, be hap - py— and joy - ful,
awe - some are— His deeds, so great is— His pow - er.

Last time to Coda

give Him— your praise. We give You— our praise.

He gives the des - ol - ate— a— home,

He leads the pris-oners out with sing -
ing. Fa-ther to the fa - ther-less, de - fen-der of the wi-
dow is God in His ho - ly place. So

CODA

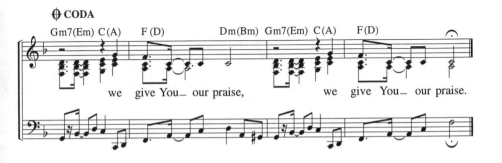

we give You our praise, we give You our praise.

———— □ ⬜ □ ————

Praise God in his sanctuary;
praise him in his mighty heavens.
Praise him for his acts of power;
praise him for his surpassing
greatness.

PSALM 150:1–2

———— □ ⬜ □ ————

96.

Let us draw near

Heb 10:22; Jas 4:8; Rev 7:14

David Fellingham

With a steady rhythm

Let us— draw near to God— in full as-sur-ance of faith,

know-ing that as we draw near to Him, He will draw near

to us.— In the ho- ly place— we stand in con-fi-

dence, know-ing our lives are cleansed in the blood of the

Lamb, we will wor - ship and a - dore.—

97.
Let Your word

David & Nathan Fellingham

Strong and rhythmic

Verse

1. Let Your word run free-ly through this na - tion,— strong De-liv - 'rer, break the grip— of Sa - tan's pow'r. Let the cross— of Je - sus stand a - bove— the i - dols of this land, let a - noin - ted lives— rise up and take— their stand. And we will glo - ri - fy the— Lamb, slain from e - ter - ni - ty.

Je-sus is Lord, we de - clare His— name, and stand in His vic-to-

ry, and stand in His vic-to - ry. ry.

Verses 2 & 3

2. With pro - phet-ic words of pow'r, ex-pose the dark - ness;— with
3. Let the Ho - ly Spi - rit's fi - re burn with-in us,— cleansed from

(v3)

a - pos - tol - ic wis-dom build the church.——— With zeal for the lost— let the
sin and pure with-in we stand up - right. Not yield-ing to wrong,. we will

D.S.

sto - ry be told,— let the shep-herds feed the lambs with-in their folds. And we will
live in ho-li-ness, bring-ing glo - ry to the Sa - viour, we will shine. And we will

98.

Lift Him up
(Lift Him high)

Capo 3 (D)
Brightly

Mt 7:7; Lk 11:9; Jn 12:32

Dave Bilbrough

2. The message of the kingdom
Stands unshakeable through time:
That man can be forgiven,
If you seek then you will find.

— □ ▢ □ —

Praise him with the sounding of the
    trumpet,
  praise him with the harp and
    lyre,
praise him with tambourine and
    dancing,
  praise him with the strings and
    flute,
praise him with the clash of
    cymbals.

PSALM 150:3–5

— □ ▢ □ —

99. Lord, I have heard of Your fame
(Remember mercy)

Capo 2 (D)

Hab 3:2

Brian Doerksen

Steadily

Lord, I have heard of Your fame,

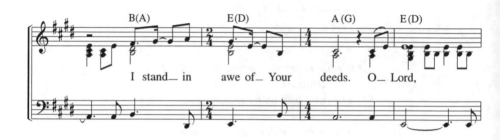

I stand in awe of Your deeds. O Lord,

I have heard of Your fame, I stand in

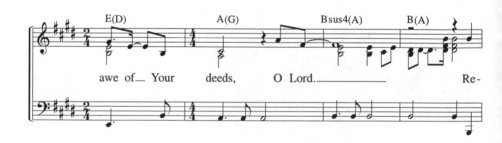

awe of Your deeds, O Lord. Re-

100. Lord, I lift Your name on high
(You came from heaven to earth)

1 Cor 15:3-4

Rick Founds

Steadily

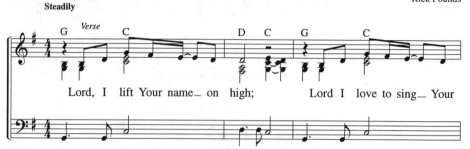

Lord, I lift Your name on high; Lord I love to sing Your

prais - es. I'm so glad You're in my life;

I'm so glad You came to save us.

You came from heav - en to earth to show the way,

— ☐ ▢ ☐ —

Though the fig-tree does not bud
and there are no grapes on the
vines,
though the olive crop fails
and the fields produce no food,
though there are no sheep in the
pen
and no cattle in the stalls,
yet I will rejoice in the Lord,
I will be joyful in God my
Saviour.

HABAKKUK 3:17–18

— ☐ ▢ ☐ —

101. Lord Jesus, You are faithful

2 Sam 22:26-27

Bev Gammon

2. Lord Jesus, You are blameless,
You are perfect, You are sinless,
Lord Jesus.

3. Lord Jesus, You are so pure,
Pure and lovely, pure and holy,
Lord Jesus.

102. Lord, look upon my need
(I need You)

Ps 51:1,7: 139:3,16

Rick Founds

Steadily

Lord, look up-on my need, I need You, I need

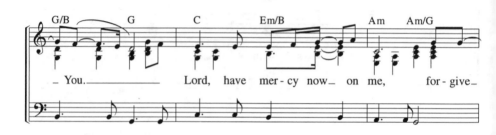

You. Lord, have mer-cy now on me, for-give

me, O Lord, for-give me, and I will be

clean. O Lord, You are fa-mil - iar with my ways,

there is noth-ing hid from— You.——— O— Lord, You know— the num-

ber of— my— days, I want to live my life for— You.———

103.
Lord of all creation

With strength

Verse

Joe King

1. Lord of all cre-a-tion, let this gen-e-ra-tion see a vis-it-a-tion of Your pow'r; put to flight all the pow'rs of dark-ness, O come, Lord Je-sus,— come. Lord of all cre-a-tion, let this gen-er-a-tion see a vis-it-a-tion of__ Your__ pow'r. Lord of all cre-a-tion, there's an ex-pec-ta-tion ris-ing in this na-tion ev-'ry__ hour.

2. Father God, forgive us
   Send Your cleansing rivers,
   Wash us now and give us holy power;
   Fill this land with Your awesome presence,
   O come, Lord Jesus, come.

*In the beginning was the Word, and
the Word was with God, and the
Word was God. He was with God in
the beginning.*

*Through him all things were made;
without him nothing was made that
has been made. In him was life, and
that life was the light of men.*
*The light shines in the darkness, but
the darkness has not understood it.*

JOHN 1:1–5

104.

Lord, we come in adoration
(Go in Your name)

Mt 28:19; Phil 2:10;
Rev 17:14; 19:16

Bright and rhythmic

Dave Bilbrough

1. Lord, we come in a-dor-a-tion,— lay our lives be-fore You
   We would seek Your awe-some glo-ry,— all the gifts that You en-

now. We are here to reach the na-tions,— to
dow. Called to reach this gen-e-ra-tion,— and

tell the world of Je-sus' pow'r.—
now is the ap-   point-ed hour,— to

Chorus

go   in Your name;   go   and pro-claim Your king-dom. Go_

in Your name, for we have been cho - sen to

tell all cre-a - tion that Je-sus is King of all kings.

2. We believe that You have spoken
Through Your Son to all the earth.
Given us this great commission
To spread the news of all Your worth.
Set apart to serve You only,
Let our lives display Your love;
Hearts infused that tell the story
Of God come down from heaven above.

3. Grant to us a fresh anointing,
Holy Spirit, be our guide;
Satisfy our deepest longing -
Jesus Christ be glorified.
Every tribe and every people,
Hear the message that we bring;
Christ has triumphed over evil,
Bow the knee and worship Him.

105.

Lord, You are calling
(Let Your kingdom come)

With expectation

Simon & Lorraine Fenner

1. Lord You are cal - ling the peo - ple of— Your king-dom to bat - tle in— Your name— a - gainst the e - ne-my; to stand be-fore— You, a peo-ple who— will serve— You 'till Your king-dom is— re-leased— through-out the earth.—

2. At the name of Jesus every knee must bow,
The darkness of the age must flee away.
Release Your power to flow throughout the land,
Let Your glory be revealed as we praise.

106.

Lord, You are worthy

Rev 4:8; 5:12

Capo 1 (E)

David Baroni

With a gospel feel

1. 2. Lord, You are wor - thy, Lord, You are

wor - thy, Lord,_____ You are wor - thy,

we give You praise. 1. praise. 2. praise._____

3. Lord, You are ho - ly, Lord, You are ho - ly,

2. Lord, You are worthy....

3. Lord, You are holy...

4. Lord, we adore You...

5. Lord, You are worthy...

107. Lord, You have my heart

Ps 27:8; Rom 12:1

Martin J. Smith

Lord, You have my heart, and I will search for Yours;

{ Je - sus, take my life and lead me
{ let me be to You a sac - ri -

on.
fice.

(Men) And

(Women) I will praise You,

I will praise You, Lord.

And

Lord.   I will   sing of love come down.

D   Dsus4   G   D/F♯   Asus4   A

I   will   sing of love come down.   And

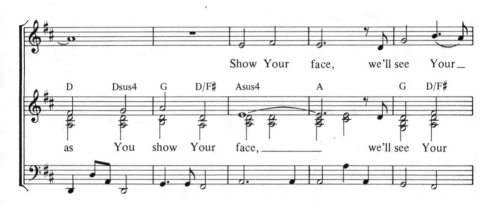

Show Your   face,   we'll see   Your

D   Dsus4   G   D/F♯   Asus4   A   G   D/F♯

as   You   show Your   face,   we'll see   Your

glo - ry   here.

Asus4   A   D   Dsus4   D   Dsus4   *Last time* D

glo - ry   here.

108.
May God be gracious to us
(May the peoples praise You)

Ps 67:1-7

Lyrics adapted by Ian White from NIV text
1973, 1978, 1984, International Bible Society
Music by Ian White

1. May God be gra-cious to us___ and bless___ us,___ make His face___ to shine___ up - on us.

May Your ways_ be known___ ov-er the earth___ and Your sal- va-tion a-mong all na - tions.

2. May the nations be glad and sing for joy,
   For with justice You rule the people You guide.
   May Your ways be known over all the earth,
   And Your salvation among all nations.

3. Then the harvest will come to the land,
   And God, our God, will bless us.
   God will bless us, and all the ends
   Of earth will fear Him.

109.   May our worship be as fragrance

(A living sacrifice)

Rom 12:1; Rev 8:4; 12:11

Chris A. Bowater

May our wor-ship be as fra-grance, may our wor-ship be as in-cense poured forth, may our wor-ship be ac-cep-ta-ble as a liv-ing sac-ri-fice, as a liv-ing sac-ri-fice. We are wil-ling

110.

Mighty God

Is 7:14; 9:2,6; Mt 1:23

Mark & Helen Johnson and Chris Bowater

In a lively half-time

Migh - ty God,___ ev-er-last - ing Fa - ther, won-der-ful

Coun - sel-lor,___ You're the Prince___ of Peace.___

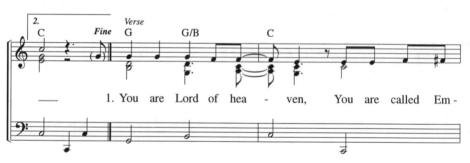

1. You are Lord of hea - ven, You are called Em-

man - u - el;___ God is now with us,___

ev - er pres - ent to de - li - ver. You are God e - ter -

nal, You are Lord of all the earth;___ love has

come to us,___ bring-ing us___ new birth._____

2. A light to those in darkness,
   And a guide to paths of peace;
   Love and mercy dawns,
   Grace, forgiveness and salvation.
   Light for revelation,
   Glory to Your people;
   Son of the Most High,
   God's love gift to all.

111.

Most holy Judge
(I'm justified)

Rom 3:22-26; 8:15-17

Steve & Vikki Cook

Driving

1. Most ho-ly Judge,_____ I stood be-fore__ You guil-ty,

when you sent Je-sus to__ the cross_____ for my sin.__ There Your__

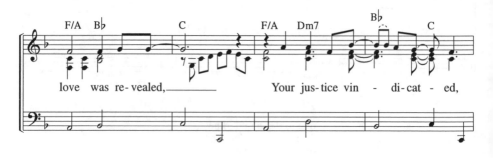

love was re-vealed,_____ Your jus-tice vin - di-cat - ed,

one sac-ri-fice__ has paid__ the cost_____ for all__ who trust__ in Je-

2. I come to You,
   And I can call you "Father",
   There is no fear
   There is no shame before You.
   For by Your gift of grace
   Now I am one of Your children,
   An heir with those who bear Your name,
   And share the hope of glory.

112.

Mukti Dil-aye
(He saves)

Lk 2:7; Acts 4:12; Rom 3:25

Author unknown

Muk - ti dil - a - ye Ye - su naam,_____ Shan - ti dil - a - ye Ye - su
Peace comes to you in Je - sus' name,_____ sal - va - tion in no oth - er

naam.
name.

1. Ye - su da - ya___ ka be - h - ta___ sa - gar,___
2. Cha - r(e) - ni main too - ney jan - am - (e) li - ya Ye - su:
3. Ham - (e) sab - (e) key___ pa - pon___ ko mi - ta - ne:___
4. Krus___ par - (e) ap - (e) - na khoon - (e) ba - haa kar:

Ye - su da - ya___ ka be - h - ta___ sa - gar,
Cha - r(e) - ni main too - ney jan - an - (e) li - ya Ye - su.
Ham - (e) sab - (e) key___ pa - pon___ ka mi - ta - ne.___
Krus___ par - (e) ap - (e) - na khoon - (e) ba - haa kar___

Ye - su hai da - ta ma - han,_____
Soo - ley pay ki - ya vish - (e) - ram,_____
Ye - su hu - a hai ba - li - dan,_____
sa - re chu - ka - ya___ daam,_____

C   D

Ye	-	su	hai	da	-	ta	ma	-	han.
Soo	-	ley	pay	ki	- ya	vish -	(e)	-	ram.
Ye	-	su	hu	- a	hai	ba	- li	-	dan.
Sa	-	ra - chu	- ka	-	ya				daam.

Translation

Peace comes to you in Jesus' name,
Salvation in no other name.

Jesus is the Ocean of Grace:
You are majestic, Lord.

Jesus, You were born in a manger (made of wood:)
You were crucified on the cross (made of wood.)

For the remission of our sins,
Jesus has been sacrificed on the cross.

By shedding Your blood on the cross,
You paid the full price for our sins.

113.

My God is so big

Gen 18:14; Job 42:2

Author unknown
Arr. Stuart Townend

1. My God is so big, so strong and so migh-ty, there's

no-thing that He can-not do._____ My God is so big, so

strong and so migh-ty, there's no - thing that He can - not

do._____ The ri-vers are His, the moun-tains are His, the

stars are His hand-i-work too._____ My God is so big, so strong and so migh-ty, there's no-thing that He can-not do._____

2. My God is so big, so strong and so mighty,
   There's nothing that He cannot do.
   My God is so big, so strong and so mighty,
   There's nothing that He cannot do.
   He's called you to live for Him every day,
   In all that you say and you do.
   My God is so big, so strong and so mighty,
   There's nothing that He cannot do.

114.

My heart

Ps 34:4

Chris Williams

My heart,— I want to give You my heart,— in ser-vice to the Lord, the One who cares—— to ask for my life. Take me,— mould my life and make me— in-to a child who longs to stay by Your side—— and learn of Your— — ways. For when I sought You, Lord,— You heard—

115.

My heart is full
(All the glory)

Ps 45:1-4, 6-8;
Heb 1:8-9; Rev 4:11

Graham Kendrick

Moderately

1. *(Men)* My heart is full of ad - mir - a - tion for You, my Lord, my God and King.

(All) Your ex - cel -lence, my in - spi - ra - tion, Your words of grace have made my spi - rit sing.

All __ the glo - ry, hon - our and

pow'r be - long to You, be - long to You. Je - sus, Sav - iour, a - noint - ed One, I wor - ship You, I wor - ship You.

2. You love what's right and hate what's evil, *(Men)*
   Therefore Your God sets You on high,
   And on Your head pours oil of gladness, *(Women)*
   While fragrance fills Your royal palaces.

3. Your throne, O God, will last forever, *(All)*
   Justice will be Your royal decree.
   In majesty, ride out victorious,
   For righteousness, truth and humility.

116.

My hope is built
(On Christ the solid Rock)

Capo 2 (D)

Mt 7:24,26; Lk 6:48-49
1 Thess 4:16; Heb 6:19

Slowly

Trad.

1. My hope is built on no-thing less
2. When dark-ness veils His love-ly face,

than Je-sus' blood and right-eous - ness.
I rest on His un-chang-ing grace.

I dare not trust the sweet-est frame,
In ev-'ry high and storm-y gale

but whol-ly lean on Je-sus' name.
my an-chor holds with-in the veil.

2. His oath, His covenant, His blood
   Supports me in the 'whelming flood.
   When all around my soul gives way,
   He then is all my hope and stay.

3. When He shall come with trumpet sound,
   O may I then in Him be found;
   Dressed in His righteousness alone,
   Faultless to stand before the throne.

Edward Mote (1797-1874)

117.
My lips shall praise You
(Restorer of my soul)

Ps 23:3; 63:5; 1Jn 4:18

Capo 3 (D)

With energy

Noel & Tricia Richards

My lips_ shall praise You,_ my_ great Re - deem-er;_

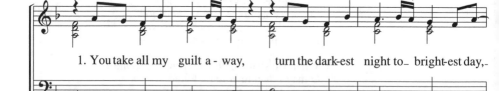

my heart_ will wor- ship_ Al - might- y Sav - iour.

1. You take all my guilt a - way, turn the dark-est night to_ bright-est day,_

You are the re - stor- er of_ my soul.

Sav - iour.

2. Love that conquers every fear,
   In the midst of trouble You draw near,
   You are the restorer of my soul.

3. You're the source of happiness
   Bringing peace when I am in distress,
   You are the restorer of my soul.

118. Never let my heart grow cold

Capo 2(D)

Chris Roe

Nev-er let my heart grow cold.
Lord, help me to love You with a love that nev-er dies.
Set my heart a-blaze with a burn-ing de-sire
to see Je-sus glo-ri-fied,
to see Je-sus glo-ri-fied.

119.
New covenant people

Heb 12:22-24,29; 13:15

David Fellingham

With life

1. New cov-en-ant peo - ple re-joice,___ lift up your eyes___ and

see your King.___ Reign-ing in pow'r___ on His heav - en-ly throne,___

ang-els are joy - ful-ly sing-ing: to the Fa - ther,

our Cre-a - tor,___ to our

Judge and Lord. And to Je - sus,

Me - di - a - tor, who has cleansed us

in His blood.

2. Let us through Jesus draw near to God,
   Offering up our sacrifice,
   Confessing that Jesus is Lord over all,
   Joining with heavenly praises:

3. We give thanks to You with fear,
   Holy God, consuming fire,
   Confessing that Jesus is Lord over all,
   We bring our love and devotion:

120.

No eye has seen

1 Cor 2:9-10,12

Paul & Rita Baloche/Ed Kerr

No eye has seen,___ no___ ear has heard,___ no

mind has con - ceived___ what the Lord___ has pre - pared;___

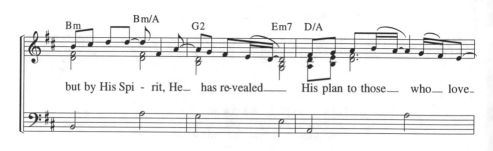

but by His Spi - rit, He___ has re-vealed___ His plan to those___ who___ love___

- Him.___   Him.   We've been held by___ His

ev-er-last - ing love,_____ led with lov - ing kind - ness by__ His hand;__

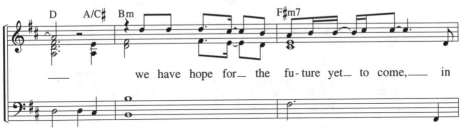

__ we have hope for__ the fu - ture yet__ to come,__ in

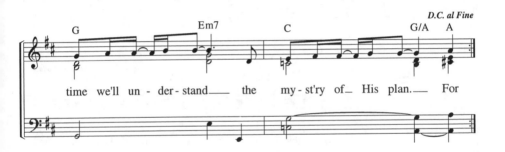

D.C. al Fine

time we'll un - der - stand__ the my - st'ry of__ His plan.__ For

121.

No other name

Acts 4:12; Rev 5:12

Robert Gay

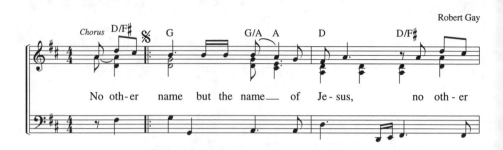

No oth-er name but the name___ of Je-sus, no oth - er

name but the name___ of the Lord; no oth- er name but the name of

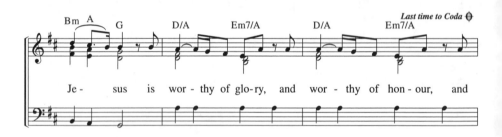

Je - sus is wor - thy of glo-ry, and wor - thy of hon - our, and

wor - thy of pow-er and all praise. No oth-er praise. His

name is ex-alt - ed far a-bove the earth. His name is high a-bove the hea-

vens; His name is ex-alt - ed far a-bove the earth, give

glo-ry and hon-our and praise un-to His name. No oth-er

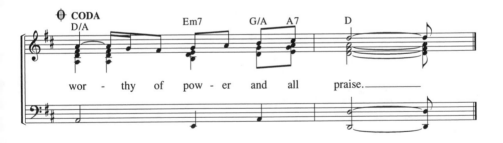

wor - thy of pow-er and all praise.

———————— □ ▢ □ ————————

*Therefore, since we have been
justified through faith, we have peace
with God through our Lord Jesus
Christ, through whom we have gained
access by faith into this grace in
which we now stand. And we rejoice in
the hope of the glory of God.*

ROMANS 5:1–2

———————— □ ▢ □ ————————

122. Nothing shall separate us

Rom 8:2,32,34,38-39

Noel & Tricia Richards

Strong and bright

Chorus

No - thing shall se-pa-rate us from the love of God.

No - thing shall se - pa - rate us from the love of God.

Fine *Verse*

1. God did not spare His on - ly Son, gave Him to save us all. Sin's price was met by Je - sus' death and hea - ven's mer-cy falls.

2. Up from the grave Jesus was raised
   To sit at God's right hand;
   Pleading our cause in heaven's courts,
   Forgiven we can stand.

3. Now by God's grace we have embraced
   A life set free from sin;
   We shall deny all that destroys
   Our union with Him.

123. O Father of the fatherless
(Father me)

Ps 68:5; 119:176;
Eph 3:15; Rev 7:14

Graham Kendrick

1. O Father of the fatherless, in whom all families are blessed, I love the way You father me. You gave me life, forgave the past, now in Your arms I'm safe at last, I love the way You father me.

Chorus
Father me, for ev - er You'll father me, and in

_ Your em-brace_ I'll be for ev - er se-cure._____

I love the way_ You fa - ther me._____

I love the way_ You fa - ther me._____ 2. When

2. When bruised and broken I draw near
   You hold me close and dry my tears,
   I love the way You father me.
   At last my fearful heart is still,
   Surrendered to Your perfect will,
   I love the way You father me.

3. If in my foolishness I stray,
   Returning empty and ashamed,
   I love the way You father me.
   Exchanging for my wretchedness
   Your radiant robes of righteousness,
   I love the way You father me.

4. And when I look into Your eyes
   From deep within my spirit cries,
   I love the way You father me.
   Before such love I stand amazed
   And ever will through endless days,
   I love the way You father me.

124. O God, be my strength

Ps 28:7; 118:14

John Paculabo

Meditatively

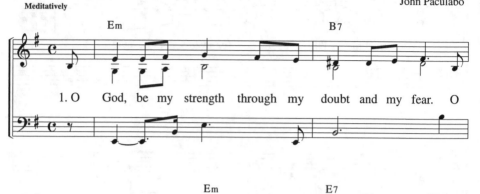

1. O God, be my strength through my doubt and my fear. O

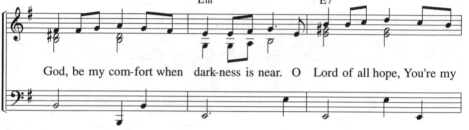

God, be my com-fort when dark-ness is near. O Lord of all hope, You're my

Sa - viour and Guide. O—— Lord have mer-cy on me.

2. O God of all mercy
And God of all grace,
Whose infinite gift
Was to die in my place,
Eternal Creator,
Redeemer and Friend,
O Lord, have mercy on me.

3. O God of all power,
Invisible King,
Restorer of Man,
My life I bring.
O Lord of my hert,
Grant Your peace now I pray,
O Lord, have mercy on me.

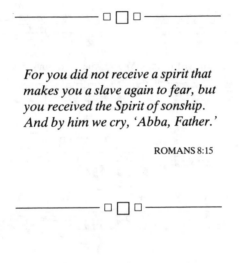

*For you did not receive a spirit that
makes you a slave again to fear, but
you received the Spirit of sonship.
And by him we cry, 'Abba, Father.'*

ROMANS 8:15

125.

O God, Most High

(You have broken the chains)

Ps 68:18; 1Cor 15:55; Eph 4:8

Jamie Owens-Collins

With strength

1. O God, Most High, Al-might-y King,—— the champ-i-on— of hea-ven, Lord of ev'-ry-thing;—— You've fought, You've won, death's lost its— sting,—— and stand-ing in— Your vic-tor-y we sing.

Chorus You have bro-ken the chains—— that held our cap-tive souls.—— You have bro-ken the chains—— and used them on— Your foes.——

All Your en-e-mies are bound, they trem-ble at the sound of Your name; Je-sus, You have bro-ken the chains. The Je-sus You have bro-ken the chains. Je-sus, You have bro-ken the chains.

2. The power of hell has been undone,
Captivity held captive by the risen One,
And in the name of God's great Son,
We claim the mighty victory You've won.

126.

Oh, I believe in Jesus
(I'm a believer)

Is 43:1

Capo 2 (G)

Chris Wimber, Carla Martin
and Tim White

2. Oh, I know He's the only One,
   Oh, He calls me by my name.
   Oh, since the day He touched me,
   Oh, I've never been the same.

127.

O Lamb of God

David Fellingham

O Lamb of God, You take a-way our sin,

You clothe us now in robes of right-eous-ness. You set us

free and pro-tect us from all harm; in ho-li-

Descant we will ov-er-come

ness we wor-ship You. And we will ov-er-come

128.

O Lord, arise
(Lord of every man)

Ps 68:1,33

Capo 2 (D)

Craig Musseau

With strength

O Lord, a - rise, re - lease Your pow'r, scat - ter Your
You hold our lives, You give us breath, You freed us

foes this ver - y hour.__ May we hold on to Your ho - ly com - mands.
from the pow - er of death.__ You're our sal -

__ You are the Lord__ of ev - 'ry man.__

va - tion, our on - ly hope,__ You are the Lord__ of ev - 'ry man.__

Chorus

Your voice,__ it is like

129. O Lord, I want to sing Your praises (La Alleluia)

Ps 63:1, 3-5

Traditional Arr. Bryn Haworth
Words: Andy Park

1st time / 2nd time

O Lord, I want to sing Your Al-

le - lu -

ia! _____

Last time Fine

G/D   D   C/D   D   G/D   D   C/D   D   G/D

G   D   C   D   G   D   C

God, You are _ my God, and I _ will seek _ You;

I am sa-tis-fied ___ when I find Your love. And I will praise ___ You as long as I live, I will lift up my hands, for Your love ___ is bet-ter than _ for Your love ___ is bet-ter than _ life. life. In Your

―――――――――― □ ▢ □ ――――――――

*I urge you, brothers, in view of God's
mercy, to offer your bodies as living
sacrifices, holy and pleasing to God—
which is your spiritual worship.*

ROMANS 21:1

―――――――――― □ ▢ □ ――――――――

130.

O Lord, You're great

Ian Smale

As a 'twist'

1. O Lord, You're great, You are fab - u - lous, ___ we love You more than an - y words can sing, sing, sing. O Lord, You're great, You are so gen - er - ous, ___ You lav - ish us with gifts when we

2. O Lord, You're great, You are so powerful,
   You hold the mighty universe in Your hand, hand, hand.
   O Lord, You're great, You are so beautiful,
   You've poured out Your love on this undeserving land.

131.

Once there was a house
(Busy little house)

Ian White

Gently

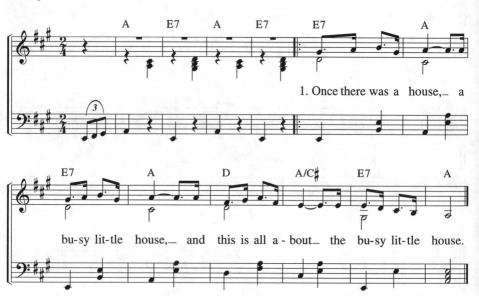

1. Once there was a house,— a bu-sy lit-tle house,— and this is all a-bout— the bu-sy lit-tle house.

2. Jesus Christ had come, teaching everyone,
   So everyone has run to the busy little house.

3. Everyone was there, you couldn't find a chair,
   In fact you had to fight for air in the busy little house.

4. A man who couldn't walk was carried to the spot,
   But the place was chock-a-block in the busy little house.

5. Whatever shall we do, whatever shall we do?
   We'll never get him through into the busy little house.

6. We'll open up the roof, we'll open up the roof,
   And then we'll put him through into the busy little house.

7. Then Jesus turned His eyes, and saw to His surprise
   The man coming from the skies into the busy little house.

8. Then Jesus turned and said, "Get up and take your bed,
   And run along instead from the busy little house."

———————— □ ☐ □ ————————

In him we have redemption through his blood, the forgiveness of sins, in accordance with the riches of God's grace that he lavished on us with all wisdom and understanding.

EPHESIANS 1:7–8

———————— □ ☐ □ ————————

132.

Only one thing

Ps 27:4-5

Maggi Dawn

1. On-ly one thing I ask of the Lord:__ on-ly one thing__
Ev-en when days of trou-ble may come,__ I will be safe if

do I de-sire:__ that I may dwell, may dwell in God's house }
God is my home,__ for I will hide in shel-ter of love }

all of the days__ of my life, all of the days__ of my

life._____ life._____ I'll gaze_____ on His

beau-ty,_____ and sing_____ of His glo-ry;_____ while

133.   O righteous God

Ps 7:1, 9-10, 17

Capo 5 (C)

Maldwyn Pope

With reverence

1. O right-eous God, who search-es minds and hearts, bring to an end the vio-lence of my foes, and make the right-eous ___ more se-cure, O ___ right - eous God. ___

Chorus

Sing praise to the name of the Lord most ___

high. Sing praise to the name of the Lord most __

high. Give __ thanks to the Lord who res - cues

me, O __ right - eous God. _____

2. O Lord my God, I take refuge in You;
   Save and deliver me from all my foes
   My shield is God the Lord most high,
   O Lord my God.

134. O Spirit of God, come down

Joel 2:23,28

Brightly, with a 'latin' feel

David Fellingham

O Spi-rit of God,— come down,— fill this heart— of mine.—

Let Your pow'r and Your glo - ry shine,—

fill this heart— of mine.——— Let the rain— from hea -

ven fall,— fill this heart— of mine.———

Let Your gifts func-tion pow-er-ful-ly____ and let Your fire__ burn_

__ in me,_____ let__ Your fire,_____ let__

__ Your fire__ burn_____ in me.

2. Burn in holiness and zeal,
   Fill this heart of mine.
   Let me now Your presence feel,
   Fill this heart of mine.
   Let the oil of gladness flow,
   Fill this heart of mine.
   Let the love of Jesus show,
   Fill this heart of mine.

— □ ▢ □ —

God raised us up with Christ and seated us with him in the heavenly realms in Christ Jesus, in order that in the coming ages he might show the incomparable riches of his grace expressed in his kindness to us in Christ Jesus.

EPHESIANS 2:6–7

— □ ▢ □ —

135.

Our Father in heaven
(The Lord's prayer)

Mt 6:9-13; Lk 11:2-4

Brian Doerksen/Michael Hansen

Quite slow

Our Fa- ther in heav- en { give us holy is Your name.
our bread.

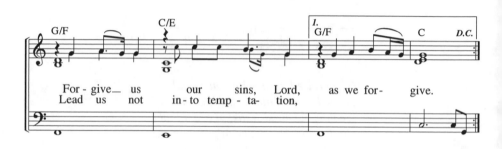

For - give us our sins, Lord, as we for - give.
Lead us not in- to temp - ta- tion,

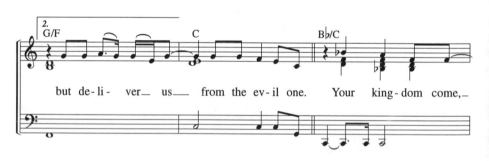

but de-li - ver us from the ev-il one. Your king-dom come,

Your will be done. Your king-dom come, Your will be

136.

Power from on high

Lk 24:49; Jn 3:3

With feeling

Ian White

Pow'r from on high, pow'r from on high, Lord, we are wait-ing— for
pow'r from on high. Pow'r from on high, pow'r from on high,
Lord, we are wait-ing— for pow'r from on high. 1. May we taste Your
heav-en here on the earth,— may Your Spi-rit bring us new birth.—

2. May we take Your heaven
   To those on the earth,
   May Your Spirit bring them new birth.

3. May the truth and power
   Of life that You give
   Very soon be ours to live.

137.

Praise and glory

(Revelation 7:12)

Rev 7:12

Capo 3 (D)

Eddie Espinosa

138.

Quiet my mind

EX 17:12; Ps 37:7; 46:10;
Zeph 3:16-17; Heb 12:12

Steadily, with reverence

Tracy Orrison

Qui - et my mind, Lord, make me still be - fore You;
calm my rest-less heart, Lord, make me more like You.
Raise up my hands that are hang - ing down;
strength - en my fee - ble knees.

May Your love and___ joy a - bound, and

fill me with Your___ peace._____

139.
Rejoice, You sons of Israel
Mt 2:11; Lk 1:68-70; 2:9,13

(The Light of Israel)

Brightly, not too fast

John Pantry

1. Re-joice, You sons of Is-rael, God has come to save His peo-ple. What joy, what cel-e-bra-tion, see our Sa-viour prom-ised long a- go. Poor shep-herds stand in awe,— as an-gel sing-ing fills the— air; and kings come bow-ing low to pay their ho-mage there. The light— of Is-ra-el

2. See Mary hold her baby,
   Son of God in her embrace;
   And Joseph stares in wonder
   At the look upon the Saviour's face.
   Yet who can see the sufferings,
   And the victory still to come;
   The path that leads to Calvary
   Rising up to heaven.

(3rd chorus) *Hallelujah, hallelujah,*
Hallelujah, praise His name.
Hallelujah, hallelujah,
Hallelujah, praise His name.

140.

Rise up

Is 60:1-3; Rom 8:19; Col 1:27;
Rev 5:8; 8:3-5; 12:11

With energy

Peter Arajs

Rise up, let Your king-dom a-rise— in us; we lift our
eyes to the skies,— and rise up to the bright-ness of— His ris-

Last time to coda
1.
2. *Verse*
- ing.

1. All cre - a-tion a- waits— the re-

veal-ing of the sons of God,— and all the an-gels of heav - en are

list-ening for the prayers of us:— Hear-ing the sound of a

pow-er-ful flood, saints of our God who've been bought by His blood.

Rise up!

2. The redemption of God has given us a kingdom view,
   And His promise to us, the hope of glory, Christ in you.
   Darkness shall run from the strength of His hand,
   Our testimony, the blood of the Lamb.

141.

Ruach

Mt 3:11; Lk 3:16; Jn 3:8
Acts 2:2; 2Tim 1:6

With a sense of awe

David Fellingham

Ru - ach, Ru - ach,

ho-ly wind of God, blow on me.

Touch the fa-ding em - bers, breathe on me.

Fan in-to a flame all that You've placed in me.

142.

Salvation belongs to our God

Rev 7:10,12

Adrian Howard and Pat Turner

1. Sal - va-tion be-longs to our God, who sits on the throne,___ and to_ the Lamb. Praise and glo-ry, wis-dom and thanks, hon-our_ and pow-er_ and strength.

Chorus Be to our God for ev-er_ and ev - er, be to our God for

ev-er_ and ev - er, be to our God for ev-er__ and ev - er. A-

men.   2. And

2. And we, the redeemed shall be strong
   In purpose and unity,
   Declaring aloud,
   Praise and glory, wisdom and thanks,
   Honour and power and strength.

143.

Say the word

Is 53:11; Hos 6:3; Joel 2:23; Mt 5:5-6; 8:8; Lk 7:7; Jn 4:14; 2Cor 8:9; 12:9; Phil 1:6

Capo 1 (D)

Stuart Townend

1. Say the word, I will be healed; You are the great Phy-si-cian, You meet ev-ry need.— Say the word, I will be free; where chains have held me cap-tive, come sing Your songs to me, say the word.

2. Say the word, I will be filled; You my hands reach out to hea-ven, where stri-ving is stilled.— Say the word, I will be changed; where I am dry and thir-sty, send cool, re-fresh-ing rain, say the word.

His tears have fal-len like rain—

3. Say the word, I will be poor,
That I might know the riches
That You have in store.
Say the word, I will be weak;
Your strength will be the power
That satisfies the weak.
Say the word.

The Lord will see the travail of His soul,
And He and I will be satisfied.
Complete the work You have started in me:
O, come Lord Jesus, shake my life again.

144.

Seek righteousness

Zeph 2:3

John Willison

Steadily

Seek right-eous-ness,— seek hu-mil - i-ty, that you may— be shel - tered on that day.—

Verse

1. We are si - lent be-fore— You, O sol - emn Lord,— for the day— you have pre-pared— is near.— We seek—

Chorus

— right-eous ness,— we seek hu-mil - i-ty,

2. Seek His face, you humble of the land,
You who do what He commands.

145.
Send me out from here

Ps 23:5; 6:8; Mt 10:10;
28:19; Mk 6:8; Lk 9:3

With conviction

John Pantry

Chorus

Send me out from here Lord, to serve a world in need. May I know no man by the coat he wears, but the heart that Je - sus___ sees. And may the light of___ Your face shine up - on me Lord. You have filled my heart with the great - est joy and my cup is ov - er-

Last time to Coda

flow - ing. 1. "Go now, and car - ry the news to all cre - a - tion ev - 'ry race___ and tongue. Take no purse___ with you, take no - thing to eat for He will sup - ply___ your needs."

CODA

flow - ing with love.

2. "Go now, bearing the light, living for others,
Fearlessly walking into the night;
Take no thought for your lives, like lambs among wolves,
Full of the Spirit, ready to die."

146. Shining forth is Your mercy
(Pour out Your Spirit)

Is 61:1-2; Mt 11:5;
Lk 4:18; 7:22

Bob Branch

147.

Show me, dear Lord
(Precious child)

Capo 2 (G)

Ps 103:10-11,13; Is 43:1; Lam 3:22; Eph 1:4; 1Pet 2:4

Andy Park

1. Show me, dear Lord, how You see me in Your eyes, so that I can re-al-ise Your great love for me. Teach me, O Lord, that I am pre-cious in Your sight, that as a fa-ther loves his child, so You love me.

2. Show me, dear Lord, that I can never earn Your love,
   That a gift cannot be earned, only given.
   Teach me, O Lord, that Your love will never fade,
   That I can never drive away Your great mercy.

148.

Sing to the Lord
(Awaken the dawn)

Deut 6:5; Ps 57:8; 108:1-2
Mt 22:37; Mk 12:30; Lk 10;27

Capo 3 (D)

With a lilt

Stuart Garrard

1. Sing to the Lord— with all of your heart; sing of the glo - ry that's

due to His name. Sing to the Lord— with all of your soul,

join all of heav-en and earth to pro-claim: You are the Lord,— the

Sa - viour of all,— God of cre-a-tion, we praise You.

We sing the songs— that a - wa-ken the dawn,— God of cre-a - tion, we

praise You.

2. Sing to the Lord with all of your mind,
   With understanding give thanks to the King.
   Sing to the Lord with all of your strength,
   Living our lives as a praise offering.

149.

Sound the trumpet

Ps 24:7; 150:3; Rev 1:18

Strong and rhythmic

Dave Bilbrough

Sound the trum-pet, strike the drum, see the King of glo-ry come, join the prai-ses ris-ing from the peo-ple of the Lord. Let your voic-es now be heard, un-re-strained and un-re-served, pre-pare the way_ for His re-turn,_ You peo-ple of the Lord. Sing Je-sus is

150.

Speak now, Jesus

1 Sam 3:10; Ps 38:15; 130:5

Craig Musseau

Speak now, Je - sus, Your ser - vant is

listen - ing. Come now, Je - sus, re -

veal Your heart to ___ me. And I'll _ still ___ my ___

heart, and set ___ it a -

151. Take me past the outer courts
(Take me in)

Ex 38:30; Is 6:6-7
Mt 5:6; Heb 10:19-20

Reverently

Dave Browning

Take me past the out-er courts,— and through the ho-ly place,—

past the bra-zen al-tar, Lord, I want to see— Your face.———— Pass me

by the crowds— of peo-ple, and the priests who sing— their praise;— I

hun-ger and thirst for Your righ-teous-ness, but it's on-ly found one place,. so take me in—

152.

Teach us, O Lord
(Break our hearts)

Job 28:28; Joel 2:13; Ps 126:5;
Prov 1:7; 9:10; Mal 3:2; Phil 2:10

Capo 2 (D)

Kevin Prosch

Light and rhythmic

1. Teach us, O Lord,____ what it real - ly means____ to rend our__ hearts in - stead of out - er__ things,____ and teach us, O God,____ what we do not__ see____ a - bout our__ hearts____ and of Your__ ways.__ And Fa - ther deal____ with our car - nal de - sires,____

2. Raise up an army like Joel saw,
   Your church that is stronger than ever before.
   They do not break ranks when they plunge through defences,
   But the fear of the Lord will be their wisdom.
   That they might weep as Jesus wept,
   A fountain of tears for the wounded and lost;
   Whoever heard of an army O God
   That conquered the earth by weeping,
   And mourning, and brokenness?
   But there will be a day when the nations will bow
   And our Lord will be King over all the earth;
   And He will be the only one,
   And also His name will be the only one.

—— □ ▢ □ ——

*Speak to one another with psalms,
hymns and spiritual songs. Sing and
make music in your heart to the Lord,
always giving thanks to God the Father
for everything, in the name of our
Lord Jesus Christ.*

EPHESIANS 5:19–20

—— □ ▢ □ ——

153.

The crucible for silver

1Chron 16:29; Ps 29:2; 96:9;
Prov 17:3; Is 6:6-7; Rev 17:14; 19:16

Martin J. Smith

With anticipation

1. The cru-ci-ble for sil - ver and the fur - nace for gold, but the
Lord tests the heart of this child.
Stand-ing in all pu - ri-ty, God, our pas-sion is for ho - li-ness,
lead us to the se - cret place of praise.

2. Father, take our offering, with our song we humbly praise You.
   You have brought Your holy fire to our lips.
   Standing in Your beauty, Lord, Your gift to us is holiness;
   Lead us to the place where we can sing:

154. The Lord fills me with His strength

Ps 18:32;
Prov 2:8

Merrilyn Billing

155.

The Lord has spoken
(Raise up a church)

Gen 17:8; Num 14:24

Paul Oakley

D.S. (Ch 1.)

(Chorus 2)
Oh, raise up a church who will walk by faith,
In the fear of God they overcome.
Oh, raise up a church whose God is with them,
They walk in wisdom, they fear no harm.

(Chorus 3)
Oh, raise up a church who revere Your judgements,
They lift up a banner of mercy and love.
Oh, raise up a church who'll not keep silent,
They speak of the glory of Your dear Son.

156. The Lord reigns

Ps 97:1,3,5-6,9

Joyfully

Dan C. Stradwick

The Lord reigns, the Lord reigns, the Lord reigns, let the earth re-joice,— let the earth re-joice, let the earth re-joice.— Let the peo-ple be glad_____ that our God reigns._____ The reigns._____ 1. A fi-re goes be-fore_ Him_ and

burns up all His en - e-mies; the hills melt like wax at the pres-ence of the Lord, at the pres-ence of the Lord._____ The

⊕ CODA

reigns._____ Our God reigns,_____ our God reigns!_____

2. The heavens declare His righteousness,
   The peoples see His glory;
   For You, O Lord, are exalted over all the earth,
   Over all the earth.

157. The Lord will rescue me

2 Tim 4:18

Janine Targett

The Lord will res-cue me _ from ev-'ry e-vil at-tack_and bring me

1st time
safe-ly to His hea-ven-ly king - dom. _ The Lord will

2nd time
safe-ly to His hea-ven-ly king-dom._ To Him be glo-ry for e - ver and

e - ver, a - men. To Him be

glo-ry for e - ver and e-ver, a - men.

— □ ▢ □ —

God exalted him to the highest
place
and gave him the name that is
above every name,
that at the name of Jesus every knee
should bow,
in heaven and on earth and under
the earth.

PHILIPPIANS 2:9–10

— □ ▢ □ —

158. The precious blood of Jesus
(Sacrifice of love)

Joel 2:32; Acts 4:12; Rom 10:13; 1Jn 1:9

Gently

John Barnett

The pre - cious blood of Je - sus, the on - ly clean-sing pow'r. My guilt___ and shame are washed a - way___ be-neath its crim-son___ flood. 2. The

pre - cious name of Je - sus, the name___ by which we're saved. He bore___ the cross I should have had,___ a ran - som for my___ sin.

And I'm___ for ev - er grate - ful, and I___ will al - ways___ trust___ the

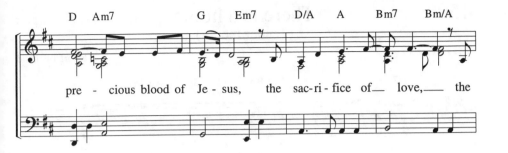

pre - cious blood of Je - sus, the sac-ri - fice of— love,— the

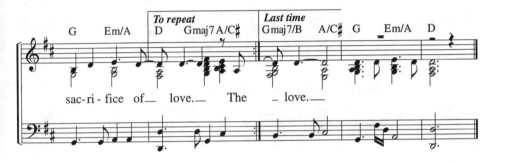

sac-ri - fice of— love.— The — love.—

159.

There is a home
(Tender mercy)

Lk 1:78-79; Jn 20:27

Flowing

Stuart Townend

1. There is a home— that wand-'rers seek, there is a strength— that
   There is a cup— that sa-tis-fies, there is a friend— who

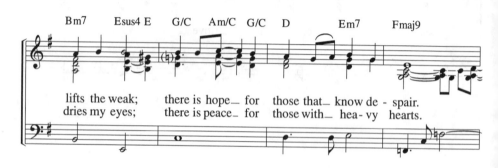

lifts the weak; there is hope— for those that— know de-spair.
dries my eyes; there is peace— for those with— hea-vy hearts.

Chorus

Ten-der mer-cy, the ten-der mer-

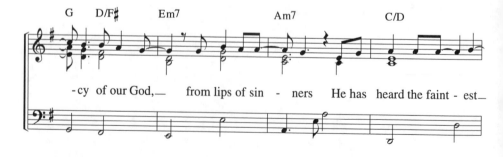

-cy of our God,— from lips of sin-ners He has heard the faint-est—

cry. Ten-der mer - cy, the ten-der mer-cy of our God,— He has re-len - ted and His grace is my de-light.—

2. I have resolved to know Him more,
He whom the hosts of heaven adore,
Mighty King, whose reign will never end.
Yet as I gaze at the Holy One,
He beckons me to closer come,
Bares the scars that show to me my worth.

160.
There is holy ground
(Holy ground)

Ex 3:5; Is 6:8; Joel 2:28;
Jn 6:68; Acts 2:17

Ian White

Steadily

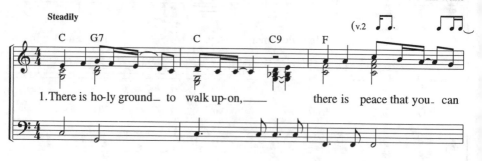

1.There is ho-ly ground__ to walk up-on,___ there is peace that you__ can

know; faith in God__ can fill your heart,___ and

fear and doubt may__ go. There is ho-ly ground__ to

walk up-on,___ leave be - hind your heav-y shoes;___

2. There is holy ground to walk upon,
   Hear Him beckon to the lame;
   For there His healing power may flow,
   And limbs find strength again.
   There is holy ground to walk upon,
   There is holy work to do;
   Trusting in the words of life,
   That Jesus births in you.
   Trusting in the words of life,
   That Jesus births in you.

3. There are holy dreams to dream upon,
   Visions from the Lord on high;
   Jesus may be showing you,
   But will you turn your eyes?
   There is holy ground to walk upon,
   You can find the Jesus road;
   Do not wait another day,
   But tell Him you will go.
   Do not wait another day,
   But tell Him you will go.

161.
There is none like You

Ps 86:8; Is 46:9; Jer 10:6-7

Capo 1 (G)

Tenderly

Lenny LeBlanc

There is none like_____ You,_____ no one else__ can touch my heart like You do.__ I could search__ for all e-ter-ni-ty long__ and find there is none like_____ You.__ Your mer-cy flows__ like a riv-

162.
There's no one like You

Ps 86:8; Is 46:9; Jer 10:6-7

Capo 2 (D)

Eddie Espinosa

Moderately

Intro. F#m (Em) | E/G#(D) | A(G) | A/B(G) B(A) F#m(Em)

E/G#(D) | A(G) | A/B (G) | B(A) E(D) *Fine* *Verse*

1. There's no one_ like

% F#m7(Em) | B(A) | Esus4(D) E(D)

You, my_ Lord,_____ no one_ could take Your_ place;

C#m7(Bm) | F#m7(Em) | *1.* B(A)

my heart beats_ to wor - ship_ You, I live just_ to
there's no one_ like You, my_ Lord,

A/E(G) E(D) | *2.* B(A)

seek Your_ face._____ There's no one_ like no one_ like_

E(D) | E7(D) *Chorus* | A(G)

_ You._____ You are_ my God.

2. There's no one like You, my Lord,
   No one could take Your place;
   I long for Your presence, Lord,
   To serve You is my reward.
   There's no one like You, my Lord,
   No one could take Your place;
   There's no one like You, my Lord,
   No one like You.

———————— □ ☐ □ ————————

*He is the image of the invisible God,
the firstborn over all creation. For
by him all things were created: things
in heaven and on earth, visible and
invisible, whether thrones or powers
or rulers or authorities; all things
were created by him and for him.*

COLOSSIANS 1:15–16

———————— □ ☐ □ ————————

163. There's nothing I like better than to praise

Ian Smale

Brightly

There's no-thing I like bet-ter than— to praise.

There's no-thing I like bet-ter than— to praise.

'Cause Lord, I love You, and there's no-thing I would

ra-ther do— than whis-per a-bout— it, talk all a-bout— it.

shout all a-bout—— it all my days.

164.
The sky is filled

Mt 1:23; Lk 2:10,13; Rev 17:14; 19:16

Capo 2 (G)

Mick Gisbey

1. The sky is filled with the glo - ry of God. Tri - um - phant - ly the an - gels sing: "Re - joice, good news, a Sa - viour is born, and life will ne - ver be the same."

2. Praise and adoration spring from our hearts,
   We lift our voices unto You;
   You are the One, God's only Son,
   King of kings forever more!

165.
This is My belovèd Son
(That the Lamb who was slain)

Is 53:11; Mt 3:17;
9:37-38; 28:19;
Mk 1:11; 4:29;
Lk 3:22; 10:2;
Jn 3:16; 4:35;
Rev 5:12; 19:7

Capo 2(Em)

Graham Kendrick

1. This is My be-lovèd Son who tast-ed death that you, My child, might live. See the blood He shed for you, what suf-fer-ing, say what more could He give? Cloth'd in His per-fec-tion bring praise, a fra-grance sweet,

2. Look, the world's great harvest fields
   Are ready now
   And Christ commands us: 'Go!'
   Countless souls are dying
   So hopelessly,
   His wond'rous love unknown.
   Lord, give us the nations
   For the glory of the King.
   Father send more labourers
   The lost to gather in.

3. Come the day when we will stand
   There face to face,
   What joy will fill His eyes.
   For at last His bride appears
   So beautiful,
   Her glory fills the skies.
   Drawn from every nation,
   People, tribe and tongue;
   All creation sings,
   The wedding has begun.

   And the Lamb who was slain shall receive the reward,
   Shall receive the reward of His suffering.

166.

This is the mystery
(Let the Bride say, come)

Song 1:15; 2:10,13; 4:1; 6:4;
Is 62:3,5; Eph 1:9,12; 1Pet 2:9;
Rev 19:7-8; 22:17,20

With strength

Phil Lawson Johnston & Chris Bowater

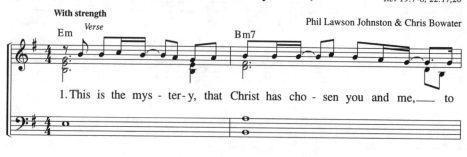

1. This is the mys-ter-y, that Christ has cho-sen you and me,— to

be the re-ve-la-tion of His glo-ry; a cho-sen, roy-al, ho-ly peo-

ple set a-part— and loved, a bride pre-pa-ring for her King. Let the

Bride say, come, let the Bride say, come, let the Bride of the lamb say,—

come Lord Je-sus! Let the Bride say, come, let the Bride say, come, let the Bride of the lamb say, — come Lord Je-sus, come! come!

2. She's crowned in splendour
And a royal diadem,
The King is enthralled by her beauty.
Adorned in righteousness,
Arrayed in glorious light,
The Bride in waiting for her King.

3. Now hear the Bridegroom call,
"Beloved, come aside;
The time of betrothal is at hand.
Lift up your eyes and see
The dawning of the day,
When as King, I'll return to claim My bride."

——————— □ ▢ □ ———————

*God was pleased to have all his
fulness dwell in him, and through him
to reconcile to himself all things,
whether things on earth or things in
heaven, by making peace through his
blood, shed on the cross.*

COLOSSIANS 1:19–20

——————— □ ▢ □ ———————

167.

To be in Your presence
(My desire)

Ps 27:4

Noel Richards

With intimacy

1. To be in Your presence, to sit at Your feet, where Your love surrounds me, and makes me complete. This is my desire, O Lord, this is my desire. This is my desire, O Lord, this is my desire.

2. To rest in Your presence,
   Not rushing away,
   To cherish each moment,
   Here I would stay.

168. Touch my lips

Is 6:6-7; Rom 12:10; 1Cor 13:4;
Eph 5:20; 1Thess 5:18; 1Pet 4:8

Chris Bowater & Philip Lawson Johnston

Touch my lips— with ho-ly fi - re from the al - tar, from the throne.— Touch my lips,— pu-ri-fy— them, may my words— be as Your own.

Al-ways life giv - ing,— thanks-giv - ing,— for - giv - ing,— al-ways be - liev - ing— and speak-ing what— is good;—

and al-ways hon-'ring,— pre-fer-ring— in love   each

oth-er, love nev-er boasts,— it al-ways cov-ers; touch my—

lips.

169.

To Your majesty

Sue Rinaldi
& Steve Bassett

To Your ma-jes-ty,— and Your beau-ty I sur-ren - der.—

To Your ho-li-ness— and your love— I sur-ren - der.—

For you are— an awe - some God who is migh-ty, You de-

serve— my deep-est praise; with all of my heart,— with

all of my life— I sur-ren - der.—

170.

We are His people
(Shout to the Lord)

Lev 26:13; Ps 42:7; 81:1;
Ezek 34:27; Nah 1:13;
Zeph 3:14; Mt 16:18

Kevin Prosch

In a steady half-time

Lyrics:

We are His peo - ple,_____
But there is a cry___ in our hearts,_____

He gives us mu - sic to sing.___
like when deep calls___ un - to the deep,___

There is a sound___
for Your breath of de - liv -

_ now,___ like the sound of the Lord___ when His
'rance,___ to breathe on the mu - sic we so

en - e - mies flee.___ But with - out Your pow - er___
des - per - ate - ly need.___

171.

We are marching
(Siyahamba)

Tr. Ander Nyberg
African Folk Tune

We are marching in the light of God,
We are marching in the light of God.
We are marching in the light of God
We are marching in the light of {God
                                  {the light of God.

We are { marching,   oo, }
       { marching, marching, we are marching, marching   }
We are marching in the light of God.
We are { marching,   oo, }
       { marching, marching, we are marching, marching   }
We are marching in the light of God.

172.

We are the army of God
(Army of God)

Capo 2 (D)

Ex 3:14; Joel 2:11; Jn 8:58;
Gal 3:7; Rev 7:14; 19:19

Kevin Prosch

With a steady rhythm

We are the ar-my of God,___ sons___ of___ A-bra-ham,___
we are___ a cho - sen gen-e-ra- tion.
Un-der a co- ve-nant,___ washed by His pre-cious___ blood,___
filled with___ the migh - ty Ho-ly Ghost._____
And I hear the___ sound_____ of the com-ing___

173. We confess the sins of our nation
(Save us, O God)

2Chron 7:13-14; Is 56:7;
Mal 3:7-11; Mt 21:13;
Mk 11:17; Lk 19:46

Kevin Prosch

Prayerfully

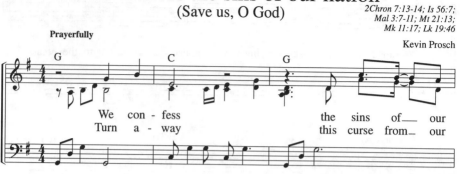

We con-fess the sins of our
Turn a-way this curse from our

na-tion, and, Lord, we are guil-ty
coun-try; we say that we've robbed You, and our

(v.2)

of a prayer-less life. We've turned a-
store-house-es are bare. O-pen

way our hearts from Your laws,
wide the flood-gates of heav-en,

that lifts up— Your name to all— the world.
let the fear of— the
let the place where— we

Lord be a stan - dard.

live be called— a house of— prayer.

— □ ☐ □ —

Let the word of Christ dwell in you
richly as you teach and admonish one
another with all wisdom, and as you
sing psalms, hymns and spiritual songs
with gratitude in your hearts to God.

COLOSSIANS 3:16

— □ ☐ □ —

174. We give thanks to you

Rev 4:8; 11:17; 12:10-11

Mark Altrogge

We give thanks— to You, O Lord,— Al - migh-ty— God,— the
One who is,— who was— and is— to— come.—
You've ta-ken up— Your pow - er and— be-gun to— reign,—
— the na-tions bow— be-fore— the Ho - ly— One.—
— Now Your— sal - va - tion,— and Your

175. We have a vision

Phil 2:10-11

Capo 2 (D)

Chris Falson

176. We have called on You, Lord

Capo 2 (G)

In a rocky $\frac{12}{8}$ feel

(Jubilee song)

Ps 30:2,4-5; Jn 1:5

Stuart Garrard

1. We have called on You, Lord, and You have heard us.
2. You have stretched out Your hand, and You have touched us,

We have called on Your name, and
sent us Your ho-ly fire, and

You have an-swered. Mer-cy has
You have purged us. Light has

tri-umphed ov-er judge-ment. Mer-cy has
tri-umphed ov-er dark-ness. Light has

tri-umphed ov-er judge-ment.
tri-umphed ov-er dark-ness.

We love

177.   Welcome, King of kings

Ps 99:1; Phil 2:11;
Rev 17:14; 19:16

Noel Richards

Brightly, with strength

Chorus

Wel - come,__ King of kings!_____ How great__

is Your name._____ You come__ in ma-jes-ty__ for ev-er__ to

reign.   1. You rule the na- tions,__ they shake   at the

sound of__ Your name. To You is giv- en__ all pow'r,

and You shall reign.

2. Let all creation bow down
   At the sound of Your name.
   Let every tongue now confess,
   The Lord God reigns.

178.

We're standing here
(This is our heart cry)

Capo 3 (D)

Stuart Garrard

1. We're stand-ing— here— with o - pen— hearts,— our

voic-es— joined— in u - ni - ty.— We know we— don't— lead per-

-fect lives,— and we cry to You— for mer - cy.

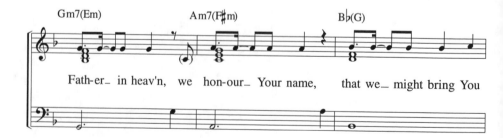

Fath-er— in heav'n, we hon-our— Your name, that we— might bring You

2. We stand before the throne of grace,
   A people for Your possession;
   We hunger and thirst, we seek Your face,
   Come touch us with Your presence.
   Father in heaven, holy and true,
   Stretch out Your hand, let power break through;
   Pour out Your Spirit upon us today,
   To heal and deliver and save.

179.

We've got a lot of hope
(Children of the great King)

Rom 5:5; Heb 12:1

David Eastman

We've got a lot of hope, — a lit-tle faith, — we've got the
pow'r of God — to run the race, — it's great to be — the
child-ren of — the great King. — We walk tall, we see
straight, we're gon-na tell the world, — we won't he - si - tate, — it's
great to be — the child-ren of — the great King. —

180. We want to see Jesus lifted high

Jn 3:14; 14:6
2Cor 10:4; Rev 8:4-5

Doug Horley

Lively

We want to see Je - sus lift - ed high,___ a ban-ner that flies_ a-cross_ this land,___ that all men might see___ the truth___ and know_ He is the way___ to heav - en. We want to see, (We're gon - na) we want to see, (we're gon-na) we want to see Je - sus lift - ed high._ We want to see, (We're gon-na) we want to see, (we're gon-na) we want to see Je- (we're gon-na)

181. We will tear down every stronghold

Capo 2 (D)

Is 40:3; Mt 6:10; 2Cor 10:4; Rev 22:2

With a strong rhythm

Dave Bilbrough

We will tear down ev-ery strong-hold through the pow-er of His word. We will seek to bring His king-dom in, make a way for His re-turn. We will tell of His sal-va-tion, for the church of Christ is

182. We will worship the Lamb of glory

Rev 5:12; 17:14; 19:16

Dennis Jernigan

183.   What kind of love is this?

1Cor 2:9; Gal 2:20;
Eph 1:5; 2:8;

Gently

Bryn & Sally Haworth

1. What kind of love is this that gave it-self for me; I am the guil - ty one, yet I go free. What kind of love is this,

a— love I've ne - ver known; I

did - n't ev - en know His name, what

kind of love—— is this?——

2. What kind of man is this,
That died in agony?
He who had done no wrong
Was crucified for me.
What kind of man is this,
Who laid aside His throne
That I may know the love of God?
What kind of man is this?

3. By grace I have been saved;
It is the gift of God.
He destined me to be His son,
Such is His love.
No eye has ever seen,
No ear has ever heard,
Nor has the heart of man conceived
What kind of love is this.

184. Where there once was only hurt

Ps 30:5,11

(Mourning into dancing)

Tommy Walker

Lively, with a 'latin' feel

Where there once was on-ly hurt, He gave His heal-ing hand; where there once was on-ly pain, He brought com-fort like a friend. I feel the sweet-ness of His love pierc-ing my dark-ness.

185.

Whose lips will plead?
(This land)

Ezek 22:30-31; 36:26;
Mt 26:41; Mk 14:38;
Lk 21:36; 2Pet 2:17; Jude 13

Alex Muir

1. Whose lips will plead for the peo-ple of this land.___ Who'll stand in the gap, and who'll build up the___ wall, be - fore the long day of God's pa-tience is ov-er, be - fore the night comes when His judge-ment will fall?___

2. And
3. And

2. And whose eyes will weep for the people of this land?
   And whose hearts will break for the hearts made of stone,
   For those who are walking out into the darkness,
   Away from God's love, without Christ, so alone?

3. And whose ears can hear what the Spirit is saying
   To those who are willing to watch and to pray?
   Pray on till God's light fills the skies over the land,
   The light of revival that brings a new day.

186. Yet this will I call to mind
(Because of the Lord's great love)

Lam 3:21-23; Rev 7:14

Carl Tuttle

1. Yet this will I call to mind, and there - fore I will hope, be - cause of the Lord's great love I've been re-deemed. The Lord is gra-cious and kind to all who call on His name,

because of the Lord's great love I've been re-deemed.

Chorus Be-cause of the Lord's great love, be-cause of the Lord's great love, (be-cause of His love) (be-cause of the Lord's great love, I've been re-deemed.

(be-cause of His love)

D.S. deemed.

2. I know of His steadfast love,
   His mercy renewed each day,
   Because of the Lord's great love I've been redeemed.
   Washed in the blood of the Lamb,
   Guiltless for ever I stand,
   Because of the Lord's great love I've been redeemed.

187.

You are mighty

Craig Musseau

Rhythmically

You are migh - ty, You are ho - ly, You are awe- - some in Your pow-er. You have ris - en, You have con- - quered, You have bea - ten the pow'r— of — death.—

188.

You are my King

Brian Doerksen

Tenderly, building in strength

You are— my King, (You are— my King) and I

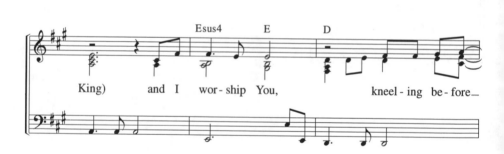

love— You. You are— my King, (You are— my

King) and I wor-ship You, kneel-ing be-fore—

— You now,—— all of my life— I glad-ly give to You.

189.

You are righteous
(You are good)

Rev 15:3

With a flowing rhythm

Wynne Goss

1. You are right-eous in all Your ways, You are good, You are good. You are truth-ful in all You say, You are good, You are good. And I bow my knee be-fore You, in hon-our of Your name, for You a-lone are wor-thy,

2. You are holy, faithful and true,
   You are good, You are good.
   You are gracious in all You do,
   You are good, You are good.

190.
You are the great I AM
(Great I AM)

Ex 3:14; Phil 2:10-11;
Rev 1:17; 2:8; 22:13

Capo 3 (G)

Tommy Walker

191. You are the one and only God

Ex 20:3; Deut 5:7;
Ps 22:3

Mark Veary

(Men) 1. You are the one— and on-ly God,
(Women) You are the one— and on-ly

(Men) there is no oth-er one— but You.
God,
(Women) there is no oth-er one— but

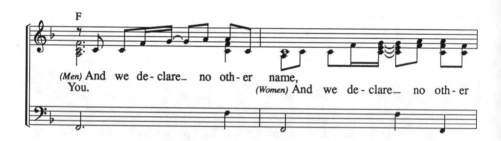

(Men) And we de-clare— no oth-er name,
You.
(Women) And we de-clare— no oth-er

(Men) Je - sus,
name,
Je - sus,
faith - ful and true.—

Be en-throned on our prais - es, be ex-alt-ed on high. See the love on our fac-es, as we glo-ri-fy, as we glo-ri-fy. Be en-throned. Your name.

2. Into Your presence, Lord, we come (echo)
   We bow before Your majesty; (echo)
   We look upon You, Holy One, (echo)
   Jesus, (echo)
   (All) Jesus.

192.

You are wonderful

Is 9:6; Rev 1:8; 17:14;
19:16; 22:13

Gently

Per Soetorp

193.   You are worthy to receive   *Is 9:6; Rev 5:12-13*

John Pantry

1. You are wor-thy to re-ceive all the hon-our and praise, Lamb of God, Prince of peace, we lift high Your— name. For Yours is the great-ness, the pow'r and the glo-ry; Lord of the na-tions have mer-cy on us. Though hea - ven be sha - ken, and earth's king-doms fall, we will still wor-ship You.—

2. In the footsteps of our King,
We walk unafraid;
Though the battle may rage,
Our praises will ring.

194. You bless my life

(Over and over again)

Ps 23:2; 119:176

Terry Butler

1. You bless my life, and heal me in-side, o-ver and o-ver a - gain.
You touched my heart and brought peace of mind, o-ver and o-ver a-gain.
All I can say is I love You. All I can say is I need You. All I can say is I thank You, Lord, for all that You've done in my life.___

2. You've been so kind and patient with me,
Over and over again.
When I have strayed You showed me the way,
Over and over again.

—□ ▯ □—

Now to the King eternal, immortal,
invisible, the only God, be honour and
glory for ever and ever. Amen.

1 TIMOTHY 1:17

—□ ▯ □—

195.

You came
(Fill the earth)

Is 61:1; Joel 2:23; Lk 4:18; Rom 5:5

Robert Newey

1. You came to heal the bro-ken heart-ed;
You came to make the blind eyes see.
Your light is burn-ing now with-in us, as Your
word of truth sets us free. And we will fill the earth with the
love of God that's been shed a-broad in our hearts, share with

2. You come in all Your mighty power,
   You come to bring the latter rain,
   We know You've filled us with Your Spirit
   And a love we cannot contain.

3. You'll come in glory and in splendour,
   You'll come to reign upon the earth,
   We know we'll live with You forever
   And declare Your mighty worth.

196. You have become for us wisdom
(All that we need)

Rom 8:10; 1Cor 1:30;
Eph 1:23; Col 1:27

Steadily

Mark Altrogge

1. You have be - come___ for us wis - dom;___

You have be-come___ for us right-eous-ness. You have be-come___ our sal-va-

tion;___ You have be - come___ all our ho - li - ness.

Chorus

All that we need___ is found in You: oh,___

2. You have become our provision;
   In union with You we have victory.
   In You we have died and have risen;
   You are our great hope of glory.

197. You have called us chosen
(Take our lives)

Deut 4:24; Rom 8:17; 12:1;
Gal 4:5-6; Heb 12:29; 1Pet 2:9

With reverence

Andy Park

1. You have called us cho-sen, a roy-al priest-hood, a ho-ly
na-tion, we be-long to You. we be-long to You. Take our lives
as a sa-cri-fice; shine in us Your ho-ly
light. Pu-ri-fy our hearts' de-sire; be to us

a con - sum - ing   fire.

2. You have shown us mercy,
   You have redeemed us;
   Our hearts cry "Father,
   We belong to You."
   You have shown us mercy,
   You have redeemed us;
   Our hearts cry "Father,
   We belong to You."

198.

You have shown me
(I give thanks)

Ps 30:2,12; Eph 2:8

Brian Thiessen

Lyrics:

1. You have shown me__ fa-vour__ un-end-ing;__ You have giv-en__ Your life for__ me.__ And my heart knows of__ Your good-ness,__ Your blood has cov-ered__ me.

Chorus

I will__ a-rise and__ give__ thanks to You, Lord, my__ God,__

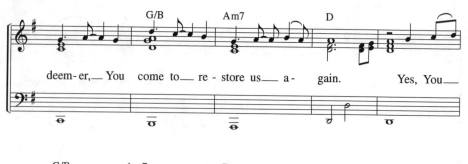

deem-er,— You come to— re - store us— a- gain. Yes, You—

come to— re - store us— a- gain, and a-gain.—

I give— thanks— to You,— Lord.

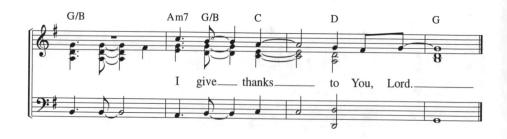

I give— thanks— to You, Lord.—

2. You have poured out Your healing upon us;
   You have set the captives free.
   And we know it's not what we've done,
   But by Your hand alone.

   We will arise and give thanks to You, Lord our God,
   And Your name we will bless with all our hearts.
   You have shown mercy,
   You have shown mercy to us.
   We give thanks to You, Lord.

———————— □ ☐ □ ————————

For God did not give us a spirit of timidity, but a spirit of power, of love and of self-discipline.

2 TIMOTHY 1:7

———————— □ ☐ □ ————————

199. You have taken the precious
(So come)

Is 55:1; 61:3; Amos 9:13;
Hag 2:6-7; Rom 8:22;
1Cor 1:27; Rev 22:17

Gently, with feeling

Kevin Prosch & Tom Davis

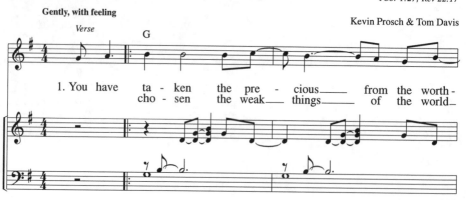

1. You have ta - ken the pre - cious____ from the worth -
cho - sen the weak____ things____ of the world____

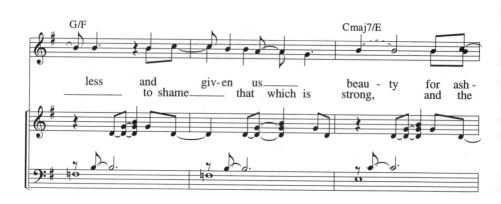

less____ and giv - en us____ beau - ty for ash -
to shame____ that which is strong, and the

es, love for hate.
fool - ish things to shame__ the wise.
You have So____
v.2 { You are
{ And the

2. You are help to the helpless,
   Strength to the stranger,
   And a father to the child that's left alone.
   And the thirsty You've invited
   To come to the waters,
   And those who have no money, come and buy.

3. Behold the days are coming,
   For the Lord has promised,
   That the ploughman will overtake the reaper.
   And our hearts will be the threshing floor,
   And the move of God we've cried out for
   Will come, it will surely come.

4. For You will shake the heavens,
   And fill Your house with glory,
   And turn the shame of the outcast into praise.
   And all creation groans and waits
   For the Spirit and the bride to say
   The word that Your heart has longed to hear.

200.

Your love, O Lord
(I will exalt You, O Lord)

Ps 35:5-6; Prov 18:10

Capo 2 (D)

Peggy Caswell

2. Your name, O Lord, it is a mighty tower;
   Your glory, it covers all the earth.
   In Your hands alone are strength and power,
   All praise be to Your glorious name.

GUITAR CHORD CHART

The following chord diagrams show the fingering for many of the guitar chords in this songbook.

Key

o = *play open string* 2 = *index finger* 5 = *little finger*
x = *don't play string* 3 = *middle finger* ▨▨▨ = *index finger bar*
1 = *thumb* 4 = *ring finger* 3 = *fret number*

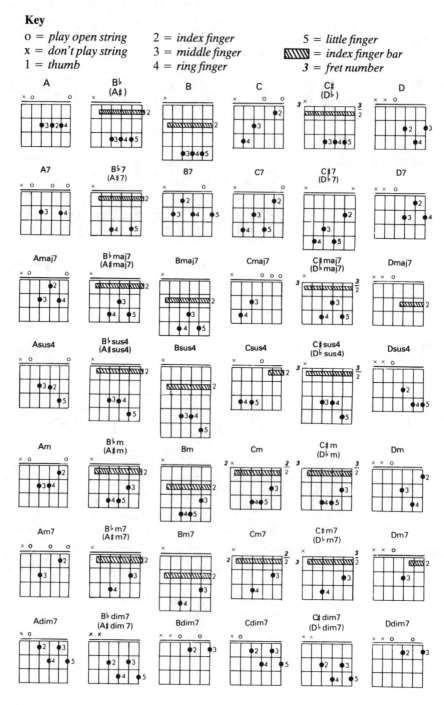

The chords which have been used throughout the book have been carefully chosen with the elementary guitarist in mind. Capo markings, in the left hand corner of many of the songs, allow simple chord shapes to be played with a capo in position. *Capo 3 (C)*, for example, means place the capo at the third fret and play the simple chords in brackets, which you will find are in C rather than E♭. If you use these capo markings you will find that you are able to play almost all of the songs using just ten chords: C, D, Dm, E, Em, F, G, A, Am, B7. If you do see a chord which you don't know, you will probably find that it is playable by mentally stripping it of all its 'extras' e.g. Gmaj7, just play G; Dm9, just play Dm; Csus4, just play C.

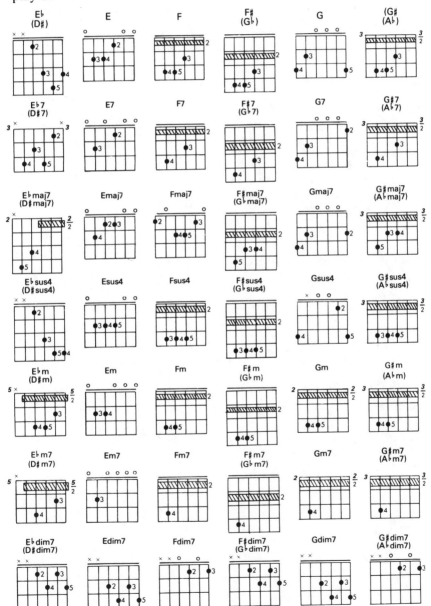

Index of titles and first lines

(Titles where different from first lines, are shown in *italics*)

Scripture index

This index lists the *key* Bible passages quoted or echoed in the songs,
and not every *passing* reference. In many cases the whole Bible passage
will repay further exploration, beyond the verses given here.

Song no.

Genesis
1:3 48
17:8 155
18:14 113

Exodus
3:5 160
3:14 .... 1, 93, 172, 190
6:15 58
15:11 48
17:12 138
20:3 191
38:30 151

Leviticus
26:13 170

Numbers
14:24 155

Deuteronomy
4:24 .... 1, 197
5:7 191
6:5 148
11:13-14 22
29:12 37

1 Samuel
3:10 150
17:4-51 40

2 Samuel
22:26-27 101

1 Chronicles
16:25 72
16:29 153

2 Chronicles
7:13-14 173

Nehemiah
8:10 67
9:5 12

Job
1:21 12
28:28 152
42:2 113

Psalms
7:1, 9-10, 17 133
7:17 81
8:3-5 49

Song no.

Psalms *(cont.)*
16:5 .... 54, 55
16:10 46
18:1-2, 7, 15-17 64
18:30 54
18:32 154
22:2 84
22:3 191
22:27-28 4
23:2 194
23:3 117
23:5 145
24:7 149
27:4 167
27:4-5 132
27:8 107
28:7 124
29:2 153
30:2, 4-5 176
30:2, 12 198
30:5, 11 184
32:7 81
34:4 114
34:8 44
36:5 28
36:5-6 200
37:7 138
38:15 150
40:1-5 77
42:7 .... 25, 170
42:8 84
45:1-4, 6-8 115
46:10 138
47:1-9 18
48:1 72
51:1, 7 102
57:8 148
59:16 84
63:1, 3-5 129
63:5 117
67:1-7 108
67:5-7 38
68:1, 33 128
68:3-6 95
68:5 .... 36, 123
68:18 125
71:22-24 83
77:6 84
81:1 170
86:8 .... 161, 162
86:11 75
91:5 84
96:4 72
96:9 153

Song no.

Psalms *(cont.)*
97:1, 3, 5-6, 9 156
99:1 177
100:5 66
103:1, 3-4, 8, 10, 13-14 14
103:10-11, 13 147
103:11-12 73
104:3-4 36
106:1 66
106:1, 6-7, 14, 43-44, 48 ... 74
107:1 66
108:1-2 148
118:1, 29 66
118:14 124
119:176 .... 123, 194
126:5 152
130:5 150
135:3 66
136:1 66
138:1-3, 8 82
139:3, 16 102
139:23 25
145:1-2, 13 80
145:3 72
150:3 149

Proverbs
1:7 .... 80, 152
1:15 166
2:8 154
2:10, 13 166
4:1 166
6:4 166
9:10 .... 80, 152
17:3 153
18:10 .... 12, 200

Song of Songs
1:2 73
2:14 47
2:16 37
4:10 73

Isaiah
6:6-7 .... 151, 153, 168
6:8 .... 69, 145, 160
7:14 .... 70, 110
8:17 84
9:2 70
9:2, 6 110
9:6 .... 192, 193
9:7 5
40:3 181
43:1 .... 126, 147

Thematic index

The following index is designed to help church leaders, worship leaders and musicians find songs and hymns appropriate for various themes, settings or occasions.
It should be noted that this is by no means an exhaustive listing, and many of the categories inevitably overlap. When looking for a particular theme, it is recommended that several associated categories are considered, rather than just one.

The 'seasonal' section has been kept short deliberately. Apart from Easter and Christmas most other occasions in the church calendar will be covered by themes already listed below.

A. GOD THE FATHER

1. General
2. Creation
3. God's love and faithfulness
4. Salvation and protection
5. God's grace
6. Forgiveness
7. Thirst for God
8. His presence

B. JESUS

1. Kingship
2. Nativity
3. The cross and redemption
4. Sacrifice (the Lamb)
5. Second coming
6. His name
7. Resurrection

C. HOLY SPIRIT

1. His presence
2. Peace
3. Holiness
4. Power
5. Fullness

D. CHURCH

1. General
2. Call to worship
3. Praise and thanksgiving
4. Proclamation and evangelism
5. Worship and adoration
6. Confession and repentance
7. Communion
8. Commission and revival
9. Commitment
10. Healing and personal renewal
11. Spiritual warfare
12. Justice
13. Prayer

E. CHILDREN

F. SEASONAL

1. Easter
2. Christmas

A. GOD THE FATHER

B. JESUS

C. HOLY SPIRIT

E. CHILDREN

F. SEASONAL